CAR MECHANICS

ON

WELDING

Edited by Peter Simpson

Published by
KELSEY PUBLISHING LTD

Printed in Singapore by Stamford Press PTE Ltd.
on behalf of
Kelsey Publishing Ltd,
Cudham Tithe Barn,
Berry's Hill,
Cudham,
Kent TN16 3AG
Tel: 01959 541444

© 1999
First reprint 2003
ISBN 1 873098 49 9

Acknowledgements
Thanks to all the *Car Mechanics* contributors who have written items for this compilation, in particular Chris Graham, Jon Hill, Jim Patten and Pete Wood, and to the numerous colleges, institutions and equipment specialists who have provided facilities, advice and equipment.

INTRODUCTION

"Once you can weld, you'll never be hungry or without shelter". I first heard that around 25 years ago, from "Brian" our metalwork teacher at school.

At the time didn't quite know what Brian was getting at, but I do now! Once word gets round that you've got a welding kit in the garage and know how to use it, paying jobs tend to throw themselves at you. A patch here, a doorskin there. And maybe even a garden gate down the road, because welding has far more applications than just cars!

And if you're into car repairs or restoration, you'll find it far more cost-effective, and very satisfying, to learn the skill yourself than to pay someone else every time. You'll also then be sure of the quality.

This book is a compilation of the authoritative features on welding techniques and practice which have been published in *Car Mechanics* over the past seven years. They cover basic techniques with Mig, Tig Arc and even old-fashioned (but still the best for some jobs) gas, plus, most importantly, how to use these techniques to fix new sections and panels to your car. There are specific features on welding rear valances, sills, wheelarches, front wings and floor pans, plus a piece by one of Britain's leading experts on MoT testing on welding for the MoT.

Much of the information in this book has come from some of Britain's top colleges – where the top tutors are training tomorrow's technicians. All the writers whose work follows are subject experts too – people who've done it themselves for years and could probably (though I definitely don't recommend trying it!) create a perfect join with their eyes closed...

I hope you enjoy reading this book – but more importantly that it inspires you to learn a new skill or improve an existing one.

Peter Simpson
Editor: *Car Mechanics*

Please note that any prices and addresses quoted were current when the material was originally printed but may have changed since.

CAR MECHANICS

CONTENTS

Mastering MIG

    Introduction 6

    Good Welding Technique 10

    Common Blunders 14

    Useful Accessories 17

Welding Technologies Compared 20

The Art of Arc 24

Start Welding

    Starting with MIG 29

    Rear Valance Swap 32

    Sills & Arches 36

    Front Wings 40

    Floor Pans 43

Welding for the MOT 46

Stick-up (Structural Adhesive) 49

Metal Management

    Popular Techniques 51

    Expert Guidance – Basics of MIG Welding 56

    MIG Welders Test 60

    Gas Welding 65

    TIG Welding 69

Plastic Management – Welding Plastic 73

Secrets of Successful Welding

    Introduction 78

    Electric Arc Welding (MIG) 79

    Electric Arc Welding (TIG) 84

    Gas Welding 88

    Buying Welding Equipment 92

    Buying Gas 94

    Safety 95

Equipment Availability 96

Chris Graham introduces the technique of MIG welding

MASTERING MIG!

Part 1

Although appearing dangerous, MIG welding should be completely safe for anyone who takes the correct safety precautions and has a full understanding of what they're doing.

Probably the most serious draw-back of using steel as the major constituent in the construction of most motor vehicles is that it corrodes. When exposed to the atmosphere, unprotected steel becomes oxidised, the result of which is surface rusting. This can take place at an alarming rate, sometimes within hours under 'ideal' conditions and, once started, the process of oxidation works its relentless way into the surface to weaken and, if left unchecked, eventually break down the metal altogether.

Look at any aging car and you're likely to find evidence of rust bubbling up from under the paint or, worse still, holes in the wings and door bottoms. This is bad news for the serviceable life of the car, especially when the rot spreads to structurally vital areas such as the sills and suspension mounting points. By this stage a successful MoT test will be an impossibility, particularly since the regulations were tightened up last November. However, such deterioration need not be terminal because, as with many other forms of infection, with rusting the rotten areas can be cut out and replaced with good, solid metal to affect a complete cure.

Most MIGs are pretty simple to operate with very few controls. Selecting the power output and speed of the wire feed are the only choices to be made on the smaller units.

What is welding?

Two pieces of metal can, of course, be joined together in a number of ways. They can be riveted, bolted, crimped and even glued but, for the purposes of the MoT test and all other manufacturing safety standards generally, welding is the only acceptable way of producing the strength and durability required. In welding, the two pieces of metal being joined are actually fused together and to achieve this, as you might imagine, considerable heat is required. Supplied by either a flame or an electric arc, this intense heat is used to melt the metal, together with a filler rod fed in as the weld progresses, on either side of the join. The two then, after 'flowing' together, become one. The result, once

MASTERING MIG!

cool, is a joint that is as tough and sometimes even tougher than the surrounding metal and one which should rarely fail.

To begin with there was gas welding which relied for its heat supply on the combustion of a mixture of oxygen and acetylene gases supplied from separate cylinders. Commonly known today as oxy-acetylene welding, this technique is still quite widely used by specialists although its intricacies make it difficult to master for all but the experienced and well-practiced expert. The search for a simpler process led to the introduction of electricity as a source of heat – the result being arc welding. Although very simple, this is rather a crude process and pretty hard to perfect. What's more, like gas welding, it's a two-handed operation.

It involves an electrode which, when struck against the earthed work piece, produces a fierce electric arc that generates the heat necessary to fuse the metal being joined. At the same time a filler rod has to be introduced and both this and the electrode are consumed as the weld progresses. Now, the most critical factor in arc welding is the distance between the tip of the electrode and the surface of the metal. It has to be kept constantly correct if the arc is to be maintained. However, the fact that the electrode is being consumed all the time the arc is operating means that it has to be fed in progressively to maintain the correct gap. Add to this the fact that the whole operation has to be viewed through an extremely dark green-tinted eye protector and this makes arc welding particularly hard to get on with for many people.

It wasn't until the introduction of MIG welding that the real breakthrough arrived. At last here was a welding technique that was simpler and much more user-friendly than anything before it and one which could produce quality results time after time. 'MIG' is an anacronym which stands for metal inert gas and this really is the key to the whole operation. An electric arc is again used to provide the heat but, in this case, it's much easier to maintain because the filler wire (the choice of which is governed by the type of metal being welded), also acts as the electrode and is fed continuously to the spot being welded through a trigger-operated handset. This trigger controls three things; the current, the wire feed and the gas supply.

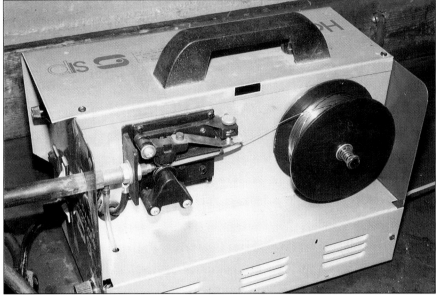
The set-up inside most MIGs is pretty much the same. Removing the side panel will reveal the wire spool and the wire tensioning and propulsion mechanism.

The spool of filler wire is held on its spindle under a spring-loaded bolt. This keeps it under tension to prevent it unwinding too much as the wire is fed to the handset.

The current is variable and, essentially, controls the power of the welder. The higher it is the more powerful the setting and the greater the maximum thickness of metal that can be welded. When welding thicker samples more filler wire will be required to produce a satisfactory joint and so the wire feed speed must be increased accordingly. This is governed by an electric motor housed within the welder itself. It propels the wire (from its storage reel also found inside the welder) via powered rollers up along the tubular cable and out through the nozzle at the tip of the handset.

The gas is also supplied via this same cable to the handset. Its function is to provide a shield around the electric arc and the weld as it's being formed. You see, at this stage the molten metal is very vulnerable to contamination. Oxidation from the atmospheric gases and other impurities picked up at this time can be very detrimental to the ultimate

It's important to get the tension properly set so that the wire feed rollers do not slip. In most cases a simple screw is used to tighten down the top feed roller to achieve this.

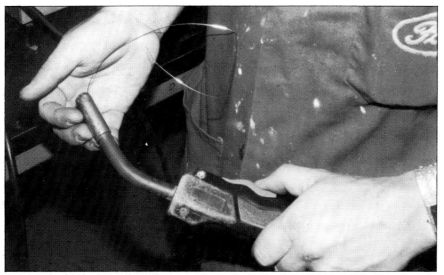

The handset has just the one control, a large, sensitive trigger. This activates the welder by switching on the current, the wire feed and the gas supply.

A useful rule-of-thumb for setting the tension of the wire feed is that it should have sufficient force to push past the palm of your hand without slipping on the rollers. More on this next month.

The smaller MIGs come with these handy, disposable gas cylinders which cost between £5-£8 and can be bought at B&Q superstores and similar outlets. The manufacturers claim that they provide 30 minutes of continuous welding. On top is fitted a simple gas regulator valve.

strength and longevity of the weld. Therefore, surrounding it with an inert gas (commonly argon), which is all but totally unreactive with anything else, affords it a tremendous degree of protection and ensures a stable environment for the weld as it's made.

The type of inert gas used does vary and, in many cases a mixture of two gases is used. As with the filler wire, the choice depends upon which metal is being welded. In some instances oxygen may be one of the constituents of the mixture. Now, as we all know, this gas is not known for its unreactivity and so, in cases where it's used, the technique cannot really be termed MIG welding. In fact MAG (standing for metal active gas) is the correct designation for welding with oxygen or, sometimes, carbon dioxide, neither of which are inert gases. Examples of the gases used include carbon dioxide/argon for mild steel (or carbon dioxide on its own), argon/oxygen or argon/carbon dioxide for stainless steel and plain argon for aluminium.

Switches and safety

Controlling a MIG welder is basically a pretty simple business so long as you fully understand the implications of what you're doing. My advice is that you thoroughly read the instruction booklet before doing anything. Don't rush in thinking you know it all because these machines can be dangerous if misused. Next month I'll be looking specifically at setting up and using a MIG welder but, for now, all we have space for is a brief introduction into the things you can push and twiddle.

Look at the front panel on any portable MIG and you're likely to find three basic controls. They'll be the on/off button, the wire speed regulator and a voltage setting switch or two. In addition there will usually be three cables issuing from this panel. One will have a plug on it for connection to a mains electricity supply, one will have a hefty spring clamp and the third, the thickest of the lot, will take the gas and wire to the handset. The cable fitted with the clamp is known as the earth lead. It has to be connected to the metal being welded to complete the circuit – without it no arc can be made.

The book of instructions will explain the relevance of each of these and should also stress heavily the importance of taking proper safety precautions. Remember that you are dealing with electricity which can shock as well as burn so always take care. You must think carefully about what you wear for welding, where and what you intend to weld and be concerned for the well-being of others nearby.

Clothing is very important. Your first requirement should be a decent pair of clean overalls which, ideally, button up to the neck. Never use an old pair of oil-soaked ones because of the fire risk. Nylon or synthetic materials are no good at all because they will melt and burn if provoked. MIG welding produces a lot of sparks, many of which will inevitably fall on the operator. The best protection against these is overalls made from a close-woven cotton material. In addition you should also never weld without gloves. Elbow-length leather gauntlets are the best and will guarantee your protection. The electric arc produces extremely intense ultra-violet light which will burn exposed skin and damage unprotected eyes within seconds.

To preserve the eyes, face and head a full-face welding mask is essential and the intensity of the arc means that a dark filter screen is also required. These are calibrated on a numerical scale with the higher numbers representing stronger, darker filters. As a rule of

MASTERING MIG!

thumb you should never MIG weld with anything marked lower than '9'. On no account ever be tempted to make do with gas welding goggles, they simply aren't dark enough. Face masks can either be hand-held or of the helmet type. The latter is more convenient because it leaves you both hands free to work with. Today you can even buy masks with light-sensitive filters which remain clear until the instant the arc is struck, at which point they become heavily tinted for complete protection. These are the ultimate although they are expensive.

It really is amazing the silly mistakes learners make when welding. There are

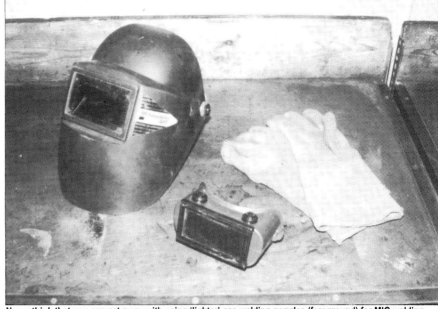

Never think that you can get away with using 'lighter' gas welding goggles (foreground) for MIG welding otherwise a condition known as 'arc eye' could be the very unpleasant and uncomfortable result.

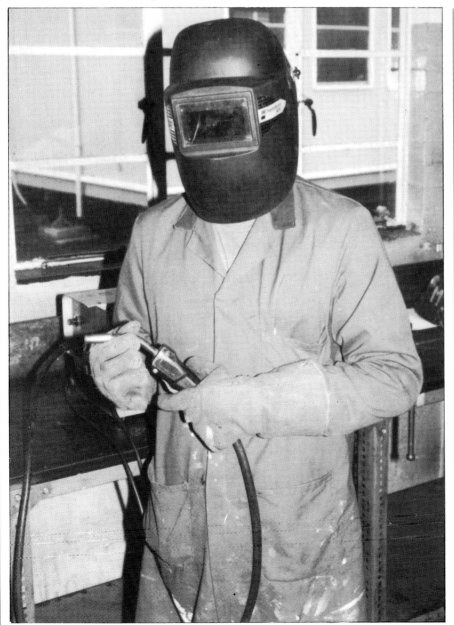

Safety is a very important aspect of MIG welding. A full-face mask is essential and good quality leather gauntlets should always be worn. Overalls made from cotton-type materials (definitely not synthetic ones) should be worn and always buttoned up. If they won't fasten to the neck make sure that all skin is covered in this region too. The intense ultra-violet light from the arc will burn in seconds.

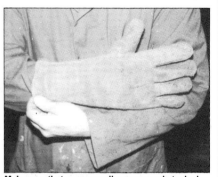

Make sure that your overalls are properly tucked into your gauntlets. Sparks and globules of molten metal up you sleeve are not funny!

genuine stories of people attempting to weld petrol tanks and even sections of chassis right next to glassfibre panel work! Both can be disastrous so take care to avoid such stupid actions. Also be on your guard for layers of under body sealant, filler or paint which may burst into flames when exposed to the arc. Never forget either that welding of this sort can produce toxic gases and so it's important that you work in a well-ventilated area. If you have to work in a confined space then make sure that you carry out the work in short bursts with plenty of breaks for fresh air

One final point regarding safety concerns the sparks produced by the MIG welding process. Don't allow these to rain down on to anything which is likely to catch fire. Pots of paint, thinners, petrol cans and oily rags are all potential hazards. This may sound obvious but mistakes of this sort are easily made, especially when you're concentrating hard on your welding and are paying little attention to what's going on around you.

NEXT MONTH
Getting started with MIG

Chris Graham explains the basics of good MIG welding technique.

MASTERING MIG!

Part 2

THE STORY SO FAR...
September:
Part 1: Introduction to MIG.

In comparison to both arc and gas welding, the operation of a MIG unit is a relatively straightforward affair. This comparative simplicity, coupled to the 'user-friendliness' of the technique, has been responsible for a spectacular growth in the use of MIG welders, both domestically and professionally, in recent years. Nevertheless, it would be quite wrong of me to give the impression that welding with a MIG is easy because it's not. There is much to be considered if good results are to be achieved and a good working knowledge of the practical aspects of the technique are essential. Armed with such awareness, though, very satisfactory results are within the grasp of virtually any user.

Getting started

I know it's a tedious way to start but the boring old advice about reading the instruction booklet before doing anything else really does have particular relevance in this case. Remember that with a MIG welder you are dealing with a device which operates by harnessing the power from a violent electric arc. This can burn you, damage your eyes, produce toxic fumes and start fires. It should never be treated lightly – a casual attitude can be extremely dangerous.

The instruction booklet, as well as detailing all the precautions necessary, should also provide valuable information on setting up the unit ready for use. This will involve connecting the gas bottle and setting the regulator, setting the tension on the wire and selecting wire feed speed together with the voltage level, all of which relate directly to the type and thickness of the metal being welded. It's important to realise that all these controls are inter-related and that it's the correct combination, as well as correct technique, which leads to the formation of a good weld.

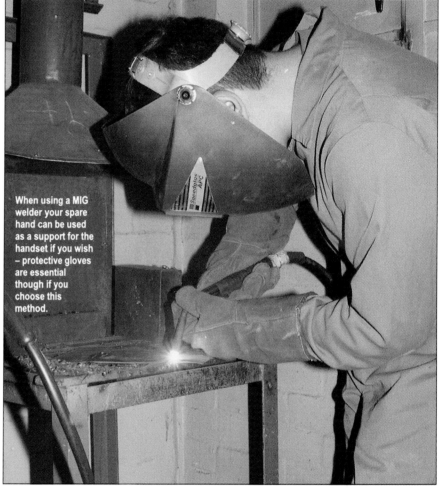

When using a MIG welder your spare hand can be used as a support for the handset if you wish – protective gloves are essential though if you choose this method.

In simple terms the voltage setting governs the length of the arc – the more volts the longer the arc will be. Linked very closely to the length of the arc is the wire speed, a fact which is obvious when it's remembered that the arc is formed between the tip of the filler wire and the surface being welded and that the filler wire is being fed to the torch and consumed by the weld all the time the arc is struck. So, in practice, if the voltage is set too high in relation to the wire speed then you will probably see the wire burning back from the surface to create a long arc. The resultant weld, or bead, will be low and flat and is likely to lack penetration. Good penetration is one of the primary aims of welding because without it the joint will be weak. For it to be satisfactory the metal being welded must have been melted and fused together through its entire thickness so that the joint is visible from the other side. Without this, complete strength cannot be guaranteed which is simply not good enough, particularly where the repair of motor vehicles is concerned.

If, on the other hand, the voltage level is set too low, with respect to the wire speed, then a short arc will be the unfortunate consequence. Now although in such cases the weld may well exhibit good penetration, the bead itself will appear thin and rounded. Under ideal conditions, with all the settings correctly balanced, the weld bead should appear as a narrow semi-circular (D-shaped in section) run with good penetration. Achieving this, however, requires practice and experience. The settings have to be juggled to suit the job and, although most instruction booklets contain tables outlining rec-

MASTERING MIG!

ommended settings, the only way to establish this is by trial and error.

BEAD SHAPE VARIATION

⟨short arc diagram⟩	Short arc, caused by high wire speed and/or low voltage.
⟨OK diagram⟩	OK
⟨long arc diagram⟩	Long arc, caused by low wire speed and/or high voltage.

One way you can tell whether or not you have the settings right is by the sound from the arc. If you hear a lot of spitting and popping then it's likely that the voltage is set too low. Now, the obvious answer to this is to turn it up but if you're working on fairly thin sheet metal then this is not advisable. An increase under these condition is likely to melt the metal and 'blow' holes which is disastrous. The solution is to increase the wire feed speed and achieve the balance that way. When the settings are correctly matched then the noise produced should resemble the sound of bacon frying in a pan – an even, continuous crackle. The golden rule to remember is that thin metal requires low volts and it's useful also to bear in mind that many professionals tend to rely on the wire speed for making adjustments. There is much more scope here for this sort of fine tuning, particularly on the smaller, DIY-type welders which have just a couple of voltage settings.

Good technique

The important thing to remember about MIG welding is that while it's vital to have the controls set correctly this, in itself, is not enough to guarantee a good weld. Technique is the key to success with a welding torch. The critical factors are the height at which the nozzle is held above the surface being welded, the angle it adopts with said surface and the speed with which it is moved.

The first requirement is that the operator should adopt the correct posture. Where possible stand in a comfortable and well-balanced manner and position the head low down and well forward, ahead of the handset. In this way a good view of the progress being made will be ensured. You see, it's important that a careful watch is kept on the performance of the arc as the weld is made. The heat generated produces a weld

The correct position for MIG welding. Assume a comfortable, relaxed and well-balanced stance and position your head so that you get an unimpaired view of the arc and what it's doing.

The wrong way to do it! This position is no good because the nozzle is obscuring the user's view of the weld.

pool which must be 'pushed' along the joint accurately and at the right speed and a good line of sight is essential if this is to happen. As far as the nozzle-to-surface distance is concerned, this should ideally be maintained at between five and 10mm.

The stability of the arc is of fundamental importance to the MIG welding process and it's governed by the distance over which it has to jump. Hold the nozzle too far away and the arc will become unstable and a sub-standard weld will result. The distance from the workpiece is also important from a protective point of view. If you remember from last month's episode, the nozzle also supplies special protective gas which surrounds the arc and the weld pool to shield the newly-formed weld and prevent the ingress of impurities.

However, holding the nozzle too far away greatly reduces this protection and lessens the effectiveness of the weld.

To maintain the correct distance from the work it helps to have a steady hand. Some people can weld one-handed but many prefer the use their spare hand for support. Positioned just under the base of the nozzle casing a well-gloved hand can be dragged along the surface of the bench to provide a continual, moving prop for the whole handset. The final point relating to the attitude of the handset concerns the angle it makes with the surface of the work. For the best results this should be kept

This spectacular close-up photograph, kindly supplied by The Welding Institute, shows exactly what goes on at the business end of a MIG welder in use. The weld pool is clearly visible and so is the next 'drop' of filler wire which is about to drop down through the arc and into the molten metal below.

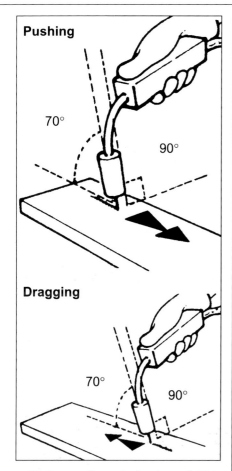

Pushing 70° 90°

Dragging 70° 90°

at 70 degrees from the horizontal. This is widely considered as being the ideal position for affording the best possible protection from the shielding gas. Holding the handset at a shallower angle would reduce the protection, while setting it more vertical would start to impair the operator's vision of the weld pool.

As if this wasn't enough, the speed at which the handset is moved is also vital. It determines the effectiveness of the weld and has to be just right. Move too slowly and the unfortunate result is likely to be holes blown in the surface caused by overheating. On samples that are sufficiently thick to withstand this extra heat the tell-tale signs are likely to be a wavering effect on the bead. Progressing too quickly, on the other hand, will result in a thin bead of weld lacking strength and penetration. Another practical indicator relating to speed of travel is the width of the discoloured area which appears on either side of the weld due to the heat produced. This is called the 'heat effected zone' and, under ideal circumstances, should extend out about 10mm on either side of the weld on samples up to about 1mm thick. If it's much wider

than this then too much heat has been generated and, if holes have not been created, then heat distortion could be another potential problem.

The effects of heat are obviously closely related to the thickness of material being welded, thinner samples being much more susceptible to distortion and damage than thicker ones. One way to adapt the welding technique to help guard against such mishaps is to vary the direction of travel. The two choices, known as 'pushing' and 'dragging' (sometimes termed 'leftward' and 'rightward'), are illustrated here and have very different effects on the material being welded. Adopting the 'pushing' method is sensible when working with thin metal because there tends to be less heat build-up. On thicker samples, where good penetration is essential, the 'dragging' technique should be used.

Careful and lengthy practice is the only real answer to understanding the foibles of the process. Given this you should develop a feeling for the settings and speed required for different jobs but always test them out on scrap samples first.

being made.

The spacing between individual tacks is important and should be varied according to the thickness of material being welded. The big risk here is one of heat distortion and it's greatest when welding thin metal sheet. Although the heat created by a MIG welder is much more localised than that resulting from a gas torch, care still needs to be taken if problems are to be avoided. Generally speaking, thinner materials will need a closer spacing than thicker ones and, as a guide, tacks on 1mm steel sheet should be about 50-60mm apart. To be safe, though, it's wise always to try the spacing out first on a piece of similarly-sized scrap to check for any distortion. It's also a good idea to grind the tacks off so that they are flush with the metal surface before final welding takes place. This will aid the smooth progress of the main weld and avoid the risk of unsightly humps.

As far as the actual joints are concerned, the most commonly used two are are the butt joint and the lap joint. The butt joint, as you might imagine, is created when two pieces of metal are butted together, edge-to-edge, and

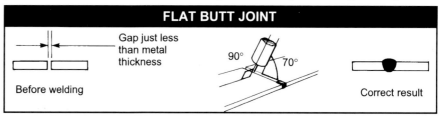

FLAT BUTT JOINT

Gap just less than metal thickness

Before welding

90° 70°

Correct result

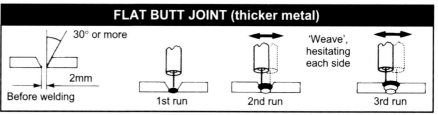

FLAT BUTT JOINT (thicker metal)

30° or more

2mm

Before welding

1st run

2nd run

'Weave', hesitating each side

3rd run

Types of joint

On a motor vehicle there are several different types of welded joint used and it's as well to be familiar with them all so that they can be practised before you start any welding for real. It's also worth mentioning tacking at this stage too. Most professionals agree that all joints should be tacked before they are finally welded. This ensures correct alignment and makes the job a lot easier and more manageable. The idea is that a series of short welds or tacks is made along the length of the joint to hold it firmly in place while the main weld is

welded. This is probably the trickiest of all the joints, especially when working with thin material, and blowing holes is always on the cards. If this is found to be a problem then a technique known as pulsing is probably the only hope for eventual success. You basically just have to adopt a stop-start action with the handset which prevents the excessive heat build-up leading to hole formation. Weld for a few millimetres then stop, momentarily, to allow the metal to cool to a dull red heat after which you start again for another short burst. It's very likely that you'll have to make use of this technique when working with small DIY-type MIGs which do not feature sufficiently low voltage settings to prevent the burning of holes.

On heavier gauge metal sheet, more the 1mm, things are usually a good deal easier although the greater thickness can sometimes create penetration prob-

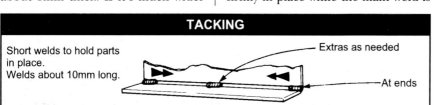

TACKING

Short welds to hold parts in place. Welds about 10mm long.

Extras as needed

At ends

MASTERING MIG!

lems if the correct allowances are not made. Good penetration ensures maximum strength and to achieve this with thicker metal sheet a gap has to be left between the two pieces being joined. The width of this should equate roughly to the thickness of the metal involved. However, where this thickness starts to exceed 2mm then the two edges will also have to be 'V'd out' as shown in the diagram. In such cases a 'multi-run' welding method must be used where an initial 'penetration run' is laid down first, followed by a couple of weaving layers over the top.

theme is the corner joint which, as you can see from the diagram, involves the joining of two pieces of metal along the pointed edge of a corner. When making such a joint it's important that a penetration gap be left between the two samples and it is vital that this gap be of the correct width – just less than the thickness of the metal. Make it too wide and the weld will sag through; too narrow and there will be poor penetration.

Finally, on the subjects of joints, it's worth mentioning the plug weld. This technique, in the absence of a spot welder, can provide a very effective and useful way of attaching body panels. A series of holes is drilled along the flange on the panel being fitted, the panel is then clamped accurately into place and each hole is systematically filled or plugged with the MIG. As with all these techniques, practice for this is essential

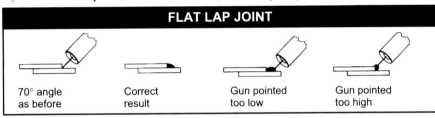

FLAT LAP JOINT

70° angle as before — Correct result — Gun pointed too low — Gun pointed too high

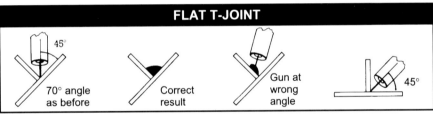

FLAT T-JOINT

45° — 70° angle as before — Correct result — Gun at wrong angle — 45°

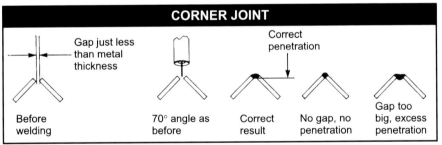

CORNER JOINT

Gap just less than metal thickness — Correct penetration

Before welding — 70° angle as before — Correct result — No gap, no penetration — Gap too big, excess penetration

The lap joint involves the two pieces of metal being overlapped and the weld being laid down along the right-angled corner that's created between the two (see diagram). With this type of joint success is governed by the accuracy with which the weld bead is positioned. The filler wire must be aimed right into the corner to ensure complete penetration. Point the handset too high and most of the weld will be deposited on the edge of the top plate with consequently weak results. The opposite happens if it's held too low and an equally bad weld is created. The direction of travel, as with butt welds, really should be determined by the thickness of the material as discussed earlier. A similar technique to that used for the lap weld is adopted for the T-joint, as seen in the diagram.

A possible variation on the butt joint

before starting the job proper. The handset should be held vertically over the hole and a small circular action adopted until it's filled. Over-filling is not a desperate problem because any excess can be removed with a grinder.

If you're interested in learning more about the art of MIG welding then The Welding Institute have produced an excellent video guide on the subject. The quality and information are superb and it's distributed by Abington Publishing. The cost is £29.95 (inc. VAT + £1.30 p&p) and further details are available on 0223 891358.

NEXT MONTH
Common welding
faults explained.

13

Mistakes are inevitable when learning to use a MIG. Chris Graham summarises the common blunders

MASTERING MIG!

Part 3

As I suggested in Part Two of this series, MIG welding, despite what the manufacturers and advertising people would have you believe, is not a particularly easy technique to master. Sure, the rudiments can be understood relatively simply by most but putting them into practice, under varying conditions, is usually quite another matter. There are many mistakes to be made and you'll probably make most of them before finally getting the hang of what's going on! According to the Mid-Kent College's chief bodyshop technician Matt Catton, the secret is not to give up and to force yourself to make plenty of practice runs before starting anything for real. Mistakes on pieces of scrap don't matter but, on a brand new front wing...

Problems, problems!

To correct any fault it's essential to understand its cause. As far as MIG welding's concerned this means developing a thorough knowledge of the workings of your welder so that when things do go wrong you will be able to make a reasonably educated guess at the reason why.

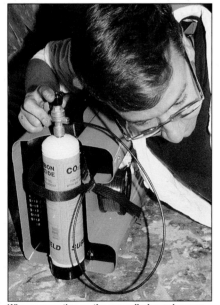

When connecting up the gas cylinder make sure that there are no leaks. Matt says that the simplest way is to listen for a tell-tale hiss. Leakages can be costly in terms of wasted gas and reduced pressure leading to sub-standard welds.

So, the first thing to remember is that most common faults fall into one of two categories; those stemming from poor technique or, those caused by incorrect control settings. Trouble from both is likely to be rife during your first few weeks with a new MIG and what follows should give you some idea of the types of problem to expect. As we've already established, the MIG welder relies upon the power of an electric arc for its operation and this arc is maintained between the tip of the filler wire (through which the current flows) and the earthed metal being welded. The filler wire is fed continuously up to the torch while the welder is working and receives its drive for this from motorised rollers inside the welder itself. Obviously, then, it's very important that the wire's passage up to the torch is not impeded, otherwise this will upset the arc and a poor weld will result.

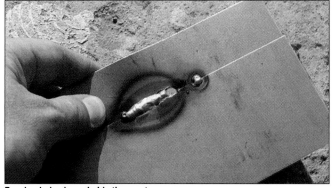

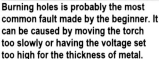
Burning holes is probably the most common fault made by the beginner. It can be caused by moving the torch too slowly or having the voltage set too high for the thickness of metal.

When working on thin material keep an eye on the heat effected zone and watch out for distortion.

A stable arc is essential for good quality MIG welding but this will be created only if the conditions are exactly right. MIG welding is all about balancing a number of very sensitive variables, all of which, when wrong, have the potential to devastate the whole process. The line between success and failure really is extremely thin as you are bound to discover for yourselves! The factors affecting the stability of the arc are the type of shielding gas being used, the distance between the torch and the metal surface and the angle at which it is held, the wire speed and the voltage setting.

One of the most common mistakes that beginners make is that they hold the torch too close to the surface. This causes the arc to burn too far back up the filler wire towards the contact tip (through which the filler wire emerges)

This is what a weld suffering from porosity looks like.

and the tip usually gets damaged. In the worst cases the tip and the wire can actually become fused together and, when this happens, everything grinds to an abrupt halt! What's more, a knock-on effect of this error is that it can cause problems with the filler wire if the tension of the rollers is wrong. You see, although such a fault may well break the arc and stop the welding, the motor in the welder will still keep working as long as the trigger on the torch is depressed. The wire will continue to be pushed up to the torch but, because of the 'blockage' at the tip, it will quickly become buckled and twisted inside its guide tube unless the tension of the rollers allows them to slip. This wastes both filler wire and time as the damaged length has to be pulled back out. It tries one's patience too!

Setting the tension of the wire feed rollers should be a pretty simply operation but a lot of beginners get it wrong. The best way to make sure that they are not gripping too tightly is to place a gloved hand over the end of the torch to block the passage of the wire, trigger the motor and make sure that the rollers slip. However, take care not to under-tension them by following the method illustrated in the photograph here.

Intermittent wire feed is another problem which leads to an unstable arc. There can be several reasons for this but one of the more common is dirt in the groove on the feed roller. Alternatively, the groove itself might be worn and distorted or there may be an obstruction

in the lining tube which guides the filler wire up the cable to the torch. For example, a build-up of metal powder in this tube can be quite sufficient to cause enough resistance to impede movement. Oxide build-up on the contact tip is another potential problem which will hinder the passage of the wire and, in particularly bad cases, there is a risk that the arc might jump between the wire and the deposits on the tip, welding the two together and, once again, bringing operations to a dead stop. Remember, though, that intermittent wire feed will usually be apparent to the operator who should be aware of the stop/start action as the weld is made. Such problems can mostly be attributed to poor maintenance.

One good indicator of how things are progressing is the shape of the weld bead and it's important that you learn to read the signs that this will present. You can learn much from its appearance and can gain valuable experience from studying the effects of different wire speed and voltage settings. For example, a flat bead with plenty of spatter (tiny droplets of molten metal thrown out of the weld to settle on the surrounding metal) indicates that the voltage is too high. If the voltage is too low, on the other hand, then the bead will appear thin, will lack penetration and, in some cases, can lead to stress cracking.

Strength secrets

A welder's greatest fear should always be insufficient penetration which, in most cases, will result from nothing more than poor technique and a general lack of skill. In particular, inaccurate torch direction is often the culprit. Remember that on the smaller welders you will be using 0.6mm filler wire which is about the thickness of a sewing needle and so accuracy when positioning this is essential. Poor aim will result in a poor weld. It's all too easy to place most of the weld on one or other side

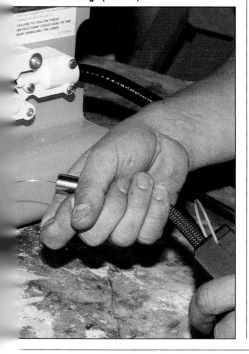
When tensioning the wire feed rollers, loop the filler wire like this as it leaves the torch and check that they are set tight enough to continue pushing it out. Don't set them so tight that they won't slip if need's be though (see text).

MASTERING MIG!

of the joint thus reducing the penetration and, consequently, the strength.

With butt welds (see diagram in Part Two) it's vital that the torch maintains a 90-degree angle to both pieces of metal to ensure good fusion on both sides and a strong joint. Fusion is also governed by the speed at which the torch is moved, as you might expect. Travel too fast and complete fusion and penetration will be lacking while moving too slowly will either lead to burnt holes or, if the metal is thick, an unnecessarily large and wasteful build-up of weld material. Now, although this will usually produce a strong weld, it can be costly in terms of the wasted filler wire and gas and there will also be lots of grinding required to clean things up afterwards. I say usually produces a strong weld because there can be cases when, once all the excess weld has been ground off, the resultant joint might be left weaker than it should be so it's best to try to avoid this in the first place.

Another disadvantage of moving too slowly can be the large size of the heat-affected zone which is likely to be produced. Not only will this increase the risk of panel distortion (bad news when working with thin body panels) but it may also be sufficient to trigger the annealing process in the surrounding metal which will, in turn, soften and weaken it.

Porosity is an additional hazard to watch for in terms of the ultimate strength of a weld. This occurs when a weld becomes contaminated by atmospheric gases during its formation and the evidence is unmistakable – the bead gets riddled with tiny holes which makes it weak and brittle. Oxygen is the most common cause and an alert operator should be able to tell by the noise of the arc that all is not well. It'll sound noticeably more 'crackly' than usual, will be hard to control and there will be lots of spatter thrown out in all directions. In such cases the route cause will usually be the gas supply system so start your checking with the cylinder and its flow meter. If the cylinder is not empty and the flow meter (if fitted) is working, then inspect the torch and check the nozzle for a build-up of spatter which might be obstructing the gas flow. If you still don't find a problem then the final possibility is that it's the surroundings which are causing the problem. Remember that the MIG process is very sensitive to drafts and it doesn't take much to disperse the protective gas shield from around the arc with costly results.

Choosing the right gas for the job is important because, as we pointed out last month, different metals require different gases for successful welding (argon for aluminium, argon/oxygen mix for stainless steel, carbon dioxide or argon/carbon dioxide mix for mild steel). Commonly, you're likely to find that the gas most frequently chosen for use with MIG welders is carbon dioxide, primarily because it's the cheapest. However, because it's a relatively active gas (in terms of reactivity), it can cause a lot of spatter. The fact that it's not completely inert means that the arc becomes turbulent and so the tiny droplets of molten filler wire, which should be falling straight down into the weld, get stirred up and thrown out to the sides in the form of spatter. Opting for a mixture of gases, say 80% argon and 20% carbon dioxide, gives a much smoother weld because the inertness of the argon literally calms things down. What's more, an additional benefit of this combination is that it leads to a cooler weld meaning that the risk of 'burn through' on thin metal is reduced.

A matter of degree

The diagrams included in Part Two of this series were not intended merely as a guide but really have to be followed to the letter if top quality results are your aim. The dreaded unstable arc can be created by a discrepancy of just a few millimetres or degrees from those quoted – it really is that critical. The problem that many beginners find is that they get the hang of the technique by welding up countless test pieces on the bench but then, as soon as they try to apply their new-found skill in anything other than the horizontal plane, it all goes to pieces. The only answer, I'm afraid, is to study the recommended positions and practise until you can apply them under all conditions.

Remember, if you hold the torch at too shallow an angle then the protection from the gas shield will be lost. Hold it too close and you're likely to damage the contact tip. Move it too slowly and holes will be the most likely result, particularly when working on thin metal. Holes can also be created due to excessive voltage and, if you find that even on the lowest setting you're still blowing away the metal then your only alternative is to adopt the pulsing technique discussed in Part 2.

The instruction booklet supplied with your welder should detail much of this information and provide additional and more specific setting-up pointers for your particular unit. Good luck!

Thanks to Matt Catton for his help with the preparation of this feature.

THE STORY SO FAR...
September:
Part 1: Introduction to MIG.

October:
Part 2: Good welding technique.

NEXT MONTH
18 MIG welders tested!

Summary of welding faults

PROBLEM	APPEARANCE	CAUSE
Poor filling		Torch moving too fast. Current too low in relation to welding speed.
Lack of fusion		Inaccurate use of torch or voltage too low.
Spatter		Voltage too high or a badly cleaned gas nozzle.
Pores		Inadequate gas shielding caused by lack of gas, faulty valve, draughts or a partially blocked gas nozzle.
Uneven joint		Welding too slowly. Current too high in relation to voltage setting.
Poor penetration		Current too low compared to voltage.

Part 5 (Final part):

Hints and tips on some of the useful accessories available for your MIG. Chris Graham reports.

MASTERING MIG!

ACCESSORIES

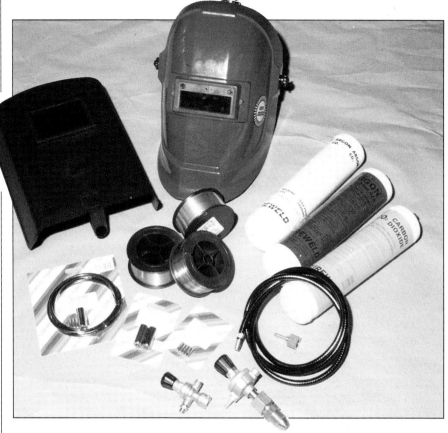

To be good at MIG welding you really do have to be a bit of a juggler! Success is all about balancing a number of important variables to create the ideal conditions under which metal can be fused together. To get it right you must appreciate fully the complex relationships between the current supply, the choice of shielding gas, the movement of the torch, the type and thickness of the filler wire and the condition of the immediate environment! Add to this the need for a steady hand, a keen eye and a cool awareness for the important safety precautions required and you can perhaps understand what makes MIG such a difficult technique to master.

Certainly most determined individuals will be able to produce some sort of a weld given enough practice but the ability to conjure up top-quality, fault-free results time and time again, whatever the conditions, is what sets the professional craftsman apart. Nevertheless, even beginners can benefit enormously from the use of good quality equipment. Like most other aspects of vehicle maintenance and repair, with MIG welding there really is no substitute for spending the money. For the best results you must buy the best equipment that your budget will allow. You'd be surprised at how often what seem like sensible savings made at the purchase stage are regretted later on.

Accessories, too, can make an im-portant difference which is why I am concluding this series with a brief assessment of what will commonly be required. With the knowledgeable help of Matt Catton at the Mid-Kent College and Geoff Ely of Sureweld (UK) Ltd (Sanders Lodge Industrial Estate, Rushden, Northamptonshire NN10 9BR, Tel: 0933 57005), I've listed some of the more practical points which should be of particular relevance to anyone new to the art of MIG welding.

Masking trouble!

Being confident about personal safety when using a MIG welder is an important consideration. Adopting a relaxed attitude will help with the success rate and one of the contributory factors towards this is a reassuring level of protection. Head and, in particular, the eyes, should take priority here and you'd be unwise to cut any corners. The ultra-violet light generated by the arc will burn exposed skin and damage unprotected eyes within seconds so always take precautions. The first and most basic line of defence is the hand-held headshield of the type normally supplied with most small MIG units. The disadvantages of these are that they leave just one hand free for welding and

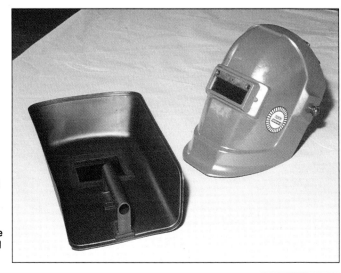

The two extremes in MIG welding mask technology. A convention hand-held face-protector (on the left) and the Wink liquid crystal autofilter welding helmet from Sureweld. The former costs about £6 while the latter's priced at around £175.

MASTERING MIG!

their construction is usually on the weak side of flimsy! Better ones are available from the specialist suppliers such as Sureweld for around £5 but really you'd be best advised to upgrade to a 'hands-free' headshield. For about £10 you get an adjustable headband which supports the hinged mask so that it's easily raised and lowered as welding progresses. Both hands are left free to support the torch, the whole face is protected and the complete assembly is light, manoeuvrable and durable. Remember, though, to make sure that the filter lens meets BS639 and that it can be replaced if needs be.

However, the big practical problem with a conventional headshield is that the only time you can see anything through it is when the arc is running, and even then it's limited. This means that the initial and all-important positioning of the torch at the start of the run has to be made with the mask raised. This in itself is not a problem but lowering the mask without moving the torch can be. The neatest solution is an autofilter welding helmet which incorporates a light-sensitive eye protector that remains clear up until the point the arc is struck. The instant this happens the light from the arc triggers a change in the filter plates (it takes just 10 milliseconds!) so they darken to provide complete protection and an ideal viewing environment.

Of course, such technology is expensive compared to the conventional headshields but the convenience and practicality factors should not be overlooked. This type of mask does away with the tedious need to raise and lower the shield repeatedly (which can be very awkward when working under a car, for example) and proves much more convenient for long stop/start welding runs. It is ideal for the beginner who

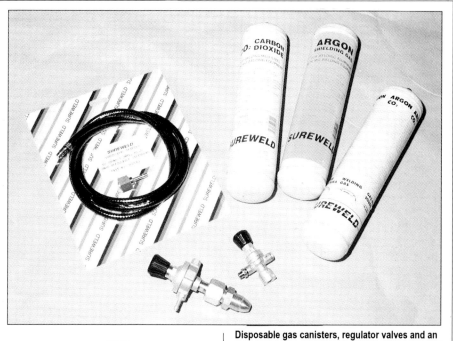

Disposable gas canisters, regulator valves and an adaptor kit. Gas canisters like this cost around £10 and are widely available. Those containing CO2 last the longest by far.

To make use of a bigger, more economical gas cylinder, you will need to buy a bigger gas regulator.

needs to see as much as possible and it can also double up as a complete face protector for use when grinding, chipping or wire-brushing.

Power to operate the filtering system comes either from batteries or, in the more expensive versions, from a solar cell which feeds off the ultra-violet light produced by the arc. Do not dismiss the battery-powered units, though, because they are a little cheaper and usually last for more than 1,000 hours before the batteries need to be changed.

A good pair of leather gauntlets, with extended cuffs, is essential, particularly for overhead work. Blobs of molten metal which find their way up unprotected sleeves make short work of burning through anything they touch, in-

cluding skin. It's also worth considering a thick leather apron if you are welding in a sitting position.

Gas choice

You should now be aware that there are a number of shielding gas options available for use with MIG equipment. We've covered the different applications in a previous episode but we've yet to consider the practical aspects of cylinder size and cost. Nearly all small DIY-type MIGs are supplied with the disposable gas canisters these days which are very convenient and available from a wide range of retail outlets. However, it's important to consider their relative effectiveness. Pure carbon dioxide, for example, fills these cylinders in pressurised liquid form and lasts up to six times longer than the gaseous alternatives of Argon or an Argon/CO2 mixture.

Nevertheless, many professionals opt for the 'mix' because of its slightly superior performance but, from a practical point of view, this relatively small advantage is pretty convincingly outweighed by simple economics. Carbon dioxide is much cheaper, is readily available and lasts much longer, relatively speaking. What's more, the results achievable with it can be every bit as good and a thoroughly satisfactory performance is quite possible.

The small gas-filled canisters will usually last for 10-12 minutes of continuous welding while the CO2-filled ones are good for upwards of an hour. If this is not enough, however, the next step is to switch to a larger cylinder for even more cost-effective operation. When

THE STORY SO FAR...

September:
Part 1: Introduction to MIG.

October:
Part 2: Good welding technique.

November:
Part 3: Summarising common blunders when learning.

December:
Part 4: A selection of MIGs put through their paces.

considering such a choice, though, it's important to bear in mind the total cost of what you're doing. You will require an addition gas regulator (say £30) to fit the larger cylinder, an adaptor (about £10) to enable this to link with your MIG and, of course, the cylinder itself. These can cost in excess of £70 to buy outright but they are refillable so this is a once-only payment.

Remember, though, that you can't go down to your local Halfords on a Sunday morning for a refill so you'd be wise to establish a local supplier for convenience before committing yourself. Your best bet is probably to stick with the pub-type CO_2 cylinders which are likely to be the most readily available and they can also double up as very useful fire extinguishers into the bargain!

Down to the wire

The other important consumable variable, apart from the shielding gas, is the filler wire. Commonly available in mild steel, aluminium and stainless steel, the choice of type is totally dependent upon the metal being welded. Most of the portable MIGs currently on the market make use of the 'mini' reels which contain 100m of 0.6mm mild steel wire. Bigger reels are available but are really only designed for professional machines subjected to regular use. Despite the fact that the mild steel wire is coated with copper it will still corrode in time so it's not a good idea to have large spools sitting around unused for long periods. For DIY applications I would recommend the use of a small spool every time. Thicker 0.8mm diameter wire is available and, in the case of mild

Sureweld, like the other welding specialists, supply a range of neatly packaged shrouds, contact tips and guide liners, all of which are available on mail order.

Filler wire is best bought in these 'mini' reels for DIY use. Mild steel should be available for about £6 but aluminium and stainless is nearer £16.

steel (the most popular choice by far), works out slightly cheaper than the 0.6mm variety! Opinions vary though about which is best for the beginner, although it is perhaps significant that all new machines are now supplied with a spool of 0.6mm.

We should also spare a thought here for the flux-cored filler wire which is designed for use in the 'no gas'-type welders. Such machines have never been high on our list of favourites but people do seem to buy them. Being re-

alistic, though, their performance is no more than that of a glorified arc welder and is not, therefore, particularly suited to serious repairs on vehicle bodywork. Add to this the facts that the flux-cored wire is very expensive and relatively limited in its supply outlets, creates lots of fumes and loves burning holes and you get some idea why most in the 'know' recommend the use of a conventional MIG every time.

Torch troubles

To conclude our brief assessment of the MIG accessory market it's worth looking at what's available to keep the business end of your welder in tip-top condition, the torch. One of the most frequent needs for the beginner will be for replacement contact tips which are easily damaged. Using the welder on the wrong setting is a common cause of this trouble but at nearly £1 a time new contact tips, while readily available, are not that cheap. The most usual problem is when the arc burns back up the filler wire and causes it to become welded on to the tip.

Another part susceptible to damage is the shroud which is the polished metal cover on the end of the torch. This features and insulator inside which cracks and becomes loose with age, at which point it has to be replaced. Again, these are pretty expensive so look after them. Don't drop them and keep them cleaned out on the inside.

Finally there is the liner which runs up inside the cable leading to the torch. Its function is to guide the filler wire smoothly up to the tip but it can get damaged if it's not treated carefully. The real danger time is when the wire is being re-threaded up to the torch when there is a risk of it puncturing the liner.

My thanks to Matt Catton of the Mid-Kent College of Technology and Geoff Ely of Sureweld for their invaluable help with this feature.

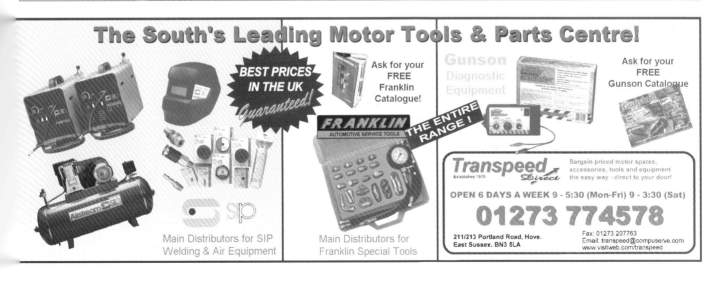

Welding Techno

Anyone who is even vaguely serious about getting to grips with the maintenance of their vehicle will, sooner or later, come up against the need for some welding. Joining metal in a safe and durable way is fundamental to the business of car repair. However, choosing the correct way of doing this, using the appropriate welding technique, is also of great importance.

There are a number of different welding methods which can be adopted for permanently fusing metal together. However, picking the right one can be more than a little confusing! For example, can a MIG be used to weld a cracked cast iron cylinder block or does it have to be arc welded? Can oxy-acetylene equipment be used on aluminium or is it better to use a MIG? What about toughened steel, can it be gas welded or is an arc unit the preferred choice?

Well, for the answers to these questions, and a few more besides, we paid a visit to our friends at Sureweld (UK) Ltd (Sanders Lodge Industrial Estate, Rushden, Northants. NN10 6BR, Tel: 0933 57005) where Geoff Ely and Richard Papworth have all the answers! What follows is a summary of our discussion.

GAS WELDING

The most traditional of the metal welding methods, gas welding using a mixture of oxygen and acetylene to generate heat is a good deal less popular now than it was 15 years ago. The advent of the modern MIG welder really dealt 'gas' a serious body blow and now it's comparatively rare to find this sort of equipment being used regularly.

This is not to say that it doesn't have its uses. As a process it's very suitable for the repair of body-thickness mild steel (with a copper-coated mild steel filler rod) and pretty adept at the joining of both aluminium and cast iron.

It can be a difficult skill to master, particularly when working with aluminium. Heat spread is the real enemy because this metal is such an effective conductor. The relative slowness of the heating effect of a gas flame (especially

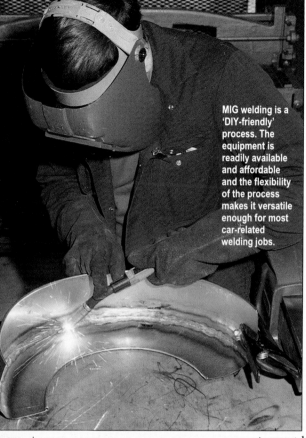

MIG welding is a 'DIY-friendly' process. The equipment is readily available and affordable and the flexibility of the process makes it versatile enough for most car-related welding jobs.

Some welding techniques are more suited to specific jobs than others, so making the right choice can be important. Chris Graham explains.

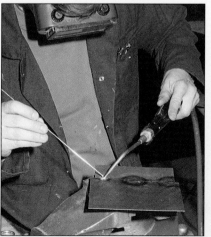

Gas welding presents more of a challenge. The technique is a hard one to master and the equipment needed is expensive. The gas can also be awkward to source.

when compared to the near instantaneous performance of an electric arc) means that a lot of heat is lost to the surrounding metal before the molten weld pool is created. In this way a large area can rapidly become very hot and, because aluminium doesn't turn red before it melts, the danger is that the whole thing can become molten and just fall apart without any real warning!

You can, in fact, gas weld cast iron but it's not really a practical proposition in the home workshop. For a start you must use special cast iron filler rods which are expensive and not readily available. The actual welding, too, is very involved because cast iron is not at all ductile and is, therefore, prone to cracking.

The localised expansion and contraction caused by welding can be quite sufficient to induce this sort of damage and the only way around this is to heat up the whole component before the weld is started. Additionally, it must be cooled very slowly afterwards and, to ensure this, it's best to embed the component in dry sand so that the temperature drops away evenly and gradually.

Generally speaking, however, the biggest drawback of gas welding, from a practical point of view, is getting hold of the equipment in the first place. The gas cylinders are usually obtained on a rental scheme and outlets for this are limited. The cost can be quite expensive and, remember, the rental has to be paid whether or not the cylinders are being used. There are also the delivery charges for the replacement gas to be considered.

Purchasing the equipment is also pretty pricey, certainly by modern MIG standards. You need decent gas regulators which will cost about £100 for starters. Add to this a couple of flashback arresters (£100), a hose set (£30) and a torch with nozzles (£30) and you're into a pretty hefty investment.

One final point concerns the storage of large gas cylinders at a private residence. Your insurance company may well have something to say on the subject so always check with them before doing anything, otherwise your house cover could be put at risk.

ogies Compared

Arc welding is probably the most versatile and affordable process of the lot. Small units like the excellent Sureweld Model 1400 seen here (refer to test, April 1994 issue) can be bought for as little as £50. The one drawback with arc welding is that it can lack subtlety and controllability, which limits its suitability for thin sheet welding in some cases.

ARC WELDING

This is probably still the cheapest form of welding with the most basic units being available for less than £50. However, it's not everyone's cup of tea and it does take some getting used to for anyone new to the technique.

In terms of versatility, though, arc welding is pretty impressive although much depends upon the quality of the machine you are using. Nevertheless, with an arc welder it is possible to weld car bodywork-thickness mild steel, hardened steel, cast iron and stainless steel.

Arc welding aluminium is not something that we would recommend although it is possible to do so. It requires special aluminium arc welding electrodes which are not easy to get hold of and are even harder to use! The coating on them is particularly partial to water and so they have to be stored in a bone dry environment at all times. What's more, they need a DC power source which makes the machinery required much more expensive and they simply cannot be used on thin material.

It is possible, as I've already mentioned, to weld cast iron with an arc welder but the importance of using the right electrode must be emphasised here. Most that are designed for use with cast iron will be based on nickel, but you should always buy the best quality that you can afford (the higher the nickel content, the better). The brittleness of cast iron gives it the potential to crack with very little provocation, as I mentioned earlier. However, the use of nickel rods can help reduce the risk of stress cracking because its relative 'softness'

helps to absorb the movement in the casting as the metal cools and contracts.

SPOT WELDING

This is a very important technique with regard to motor cars simply because it's the way that the manufacturers choose to join them together. If you are involved in the restoration or repair of a vehicle, and you want your work to 'look right', then using a spot welder will provide the most authentic results.

Spot welding is still the first choice of the garage workshop because of its relative simplicity. Having said this, though, the whole process is entirely dependent upon accessibility. The metal being joined has to be 'pinched' between a pair of copper electrodes and so, obviously, both sides of the joint need to be 'reachable'. One-sided spot

welding gives unpredictable results and should be avoided. If both sides are not accessible then MIG 'plug' welding can be used.

A current passes between the electrodes and, in doing so, travels through the workpiece. The resistance it encounters on the way is what generates the heat to form the weld. Different metals have different levels of electrical conductivity and to compensate for this the power and weld time have to be adjusted.

When using a spot welder it's essential to make some test welds on scrap metal and subject them to a 'tear test'. Pulling the two pieces apart should, if the weld is up to scratch, leave a clean hole in one piece (on the left) and a 'plug' on the other.

Spot welding is particularly suited to mild steel and you can get good results with stainless steel too. Aluminium can also be spot welded but it's much more difficult because of the extra power needed. Mild steel has a high resistance to the flow of electricity and so a lot of heat is generated leading to successful and simple welding.

Aluminium, on the other hand, is a good conductor of electricity which, accordingly, generates little resistance and low levels of heat. To compensate

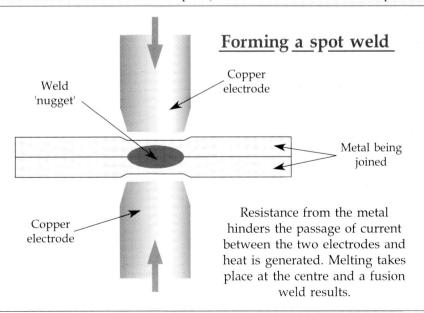

Forming a spot weld

Weld 'nugget'
Copper electrode
Metal being joined
Copper electrode

Resistance from the metal hinders the passage of current between the two electrodes and heat is generated. Melting takes place at the centre and a fusion weld results.

21

Welding Technologies Compared

Spot welding is an ideal technique for joining flanged body panels. This is the method which the manufacturers choose because it's quick, simple and very effective. Equipment is expensive, though, and not particularly versatile either.

for this you have to have much more power to induce the desired heat and ensure that a good weld is created. Unfortunately, though, this extra power means extra money, and this sort of equipment can cost well in excess of £2,000 and require a three-phase electrical supply into the bargain. Consequently, the prospects for the DIY spot welding of aluminium are very limited!

The more conventional, 240V spot welders are more affordable and can be yours for a few hundred pounds. Remember, however, that they are limited in their performance and are really only suited to the fitting of body panels and repair sections etc. They are of no use when it comes to more general welding needs, such as repairing a fractured lawn mower handle or welding up your front gate!

Purchase of a spot welder is perhaps not a practical option for the average DIY enthusiast but borrowing or hiring one makes a lot more sense. Alternatively, you can use a MIG to make a plug weld which will take on a similar appearance to a spot weld.

Successful spot welding is utterly dependent upon being able to work with clean metal. The current must flow freely between the electrodes and so it's vital for all four faces of the metal involved to be contaminant-free. If there is any rust, old paint, oil, grease or general dirt present then nothing much will happen because the flow of electricity will be impaired and the heat will not be generated.

If you are welding a new panel on to some much older metal, its thickness will vary, especially if you've been a little heavy-handed with the angle grinder while cleaning up the edge! This varia-

Top-end spot welders as used by the trade come with automatic pulse controls and all sorts of other control mechanisms for enhanced performance. The cost of this sort of gear is high.

tion is important because it will affect the consistency of the welds – some will be better (stronger) than others. These problems are heightened, of course, when you are dealing with more than just two layers of metal which can be the case when fitting sills, for example.

The other danger is that a spot weld can look perfect while actually being next to useless. Because you can't visually inspect the critical area of a spot weld (where the fusion has occurred), being certain about the weld's effectiveness can be tricky. The sensible approach is to check your technique and settings by making some welds on a test piece (similar metal, similar thickness) and testing them to destruction. Tear the two sheets apart – a good weld will leave a clean hole in one, and a circular plug on the other.

MIG WELDING

MIG welding really has become the industry standard in recent years. Sales have rocketed and units can now be found in virtually every professional workshop, plus a good many domestic garages as well.

The relative simplicity of operation, the affordability of the machines and the excellent availability which they now enjoy (most DIY and motoring superstores stock MIGs) mean that this technique is here to stay.

A cut above most ordinary arc welders, a MIG machine, even one of the cheapest, should be able to weld body-thickness sheet steel without blowing holes and, is ideal for most other car-related welding jobs too. Stainless steel and aluminium can also be tackled with a MIG (with the correct filler wire, of course) but cast iron and hardened steel are a definite no-no because suitable filler wires are not readily available. It's also worth noting that, when using a MIG to weld aluminium, the machine will have to be set up with pure argon gas (and aluminium filler wire).

The smaller MIG units are generally pretty portable which makes them convenient for home use but they are not particularly suited to operation out of doors. Because the molten weld is shielded by a canopy of inert gas to prevent contamination, the process is very sensitive to wind. Working outside on a breezy day will almost certainly result in a defective weld because the all-important protection from the gas will have been lost.

A less sensitive variation on the theme is the 'no gas' welder which works in a similar way to a MIG but, yes, you've guessed it, without the gas! The filler wire used in these machines has a flux core which, when the wire is melted by the arc, floats to the surface to protect the weld as it cools. This technique represents a sort of cross between MIG and arc and opinions vary about it effectiveness.

The 'no gas' process is certainly far less controllable and a deal more severe than MIG, which limits its applications somewhat. It's certainly very effective on mild steel generally, particularly the thick stuff. However, when rather more subtlety is required, when welding thin sheet steel, for example, these machines can be found wanting. Holes are easily blown, especially by the beginner. Consequently, 'no gas' machines are limited to welding mild steel only.

TIG WELDING

This is pretty specialised welding equipment which so far has been restricted to the professional user. It's not normally used as a DIY-type welding technique on motor vehicles but, for welding the tubular frame of a motor cycle it can be ideal.

A TIG welding machine looks much like a MIG but the torch itself (seen here on the left) is very different. Filler wire is supplied by a separate electrode so TIG welding is a two-handed operation. The process is hard to master and the hardware is expensive. However, TIG is the ideal way to weld aluminium and its controllability makes it exceptionally neat. AC-powered machines are expensive but DC models are cheaper.

The arc is formed between a non-consumable tungsten electrode and the metal surface being welded and, while it does so, is surrounded by a protective umbrella of inert shielding gas to prevent contamination of the newly-formed weld (TIG standing for 'tungsten inert gas').

This process is particularly suited to the welding of aluminium although the machinery required to do this is expensive. A good TIG unit will usually be powered from a three-phase supply and will boast a high frequency AC output which is necessary to overcome the oxide layer present on aluminium or on all aluminium alloys. The cost of a good quality machine is likely to be £1,000+. You can buy TIGs that will run off a domestic 240V DC supply but, unfortunately, these often have only a DC output which is fine for steel but useless for aluminium.

The TIG process is much harder to master than MIG. The heat produced by the torch is extremely intense and a weld pool is created virtually instantaneously, which makes it quite hard to use on thin sheet steel or aluminium. In some cases a filler wire will not be needed to aid fusion but, when it is, it has to be fed into the weld pool by hand in much the same way as with gas welding.

A DC output is required for TIG welding mild and stainless steel for which high frequency is not essential. DC machines without 'HF' are a lot cheaper, starting at about £300.

A big advantage of TIG welding can be its neatness. Using a DC machine when butt welding thin steel sheet (edge to edge) can be very effective and easier than using an arc or MIG. This is because the heat source is so localised thanks to the precise control the operator has over the arc.

Professional machines with their extra sophistication have a much greater degree of flexibility and, at the top of the range, will feature foot controls for the current. In this way the power of the arc can be varied as the weld progresses.

BRAZING

This is not strictly a welding technique because the metal being joined is not actually fused together as with all the others mentioned before. However, I think it's worth a quick mention at the end here.

Known also as 'hard soldering', the brazing process does not rely on the melting of the metal being joined and so is not as strong as a conventional

Brazing, while not strictly a welding process, is a useful and versatile technique for joining metal. However, the fact that no metal-to-metal fusion occurs means that brazed joints are not suitable for structural repairs.

weld. Instead, a bond is achieved by melting a metal alloy (commonly brass) into the joint between the metal pieces being brazed. This alloy fuses itself to the metal, rather like a solder, and a sturdy union results. A flux is required (often on the filler wire already) and the metal being joined must be pre-heated before the brass is melted in.

One of the big advantages of brazing is that it can be successfully used to join virtually any metal, although it should never be used for important, structural joints because it simply doesn't have the strength. For patching a holed exhaust, however, there is nothing to touch it!

The one limiting factor, however, is the heat source. Ideally this should be an oxy-acetylene torch but, as we've already noted, this is expensive. Alternatives include a propane/butane torch (small components only) or a carbon-arc torch. The latter is a relatively cheap solution because it can be used with most conventional arc welders as an effective source of heat. Controllability can be a problem, though, because the carbon rods are 6mm-8mm in diameter so the arc produced is pretty large. Therefore, this type of brazing is unsuitable for aluminium.

Conclusions

This introduction to the different welding techniques should have given you an insight into what's available and the importance of choosing the right one for your needs. TIG and gas are generally only found in the trade. Occasional DIY access to such equipment via your friendly local workshop manager, however, can prove very useful!

The favourites from the bunch must be arc and MIG. Both are affordable and straightforward. Arc is the cheaper long-term option as far as consumables are concerned but much depends upon the level of usage. A MIG will certainly afford its operator greater control but an arc welder is definitely the better option if outdoor use is important.

The extra subtlety of the MIG process makes it most people's favourite for car bodywork repairs. What's more, with sales competition as hot as it is at present, there are some great bargains to be had if you're prepared to shop around.

My thanks to Geoff Ely and Richard Papworth at Sureweld and to Matt Catton at the Mid-Kent College in Maidstone for their kind help with this feature.

	ARC WELDING	MIG WELDING	'NO GAS' WELDING	GAS WELDING	OXY-ACET. BRAZING
STEEL BODYWORK	OK	IDEAL	OK	IDEAL	OK
MILD STEEL	IDEAL	IDEAL	IDEAL	OK	OK
HARDENED STEEL	IDEAL	NO	NO	NO	OK
CAST IRON	IDEAL	NO	NO	OK	OK
STAINLESS STEEL	IDEAL	OK	NO	NO	OK
ALUMINIUM	NO	IDEAL	NO	OK	OK

The ART of ARC

Chris Graham investigates the pros and cons of this affordable welding technique.

Safety precautions are important when using an arc welder. Always wear good quality overalls which fasten up to the neck to prevent sparks and molten blobs of metal falling down inside your clothing. Ear plugs are also a sensible idea and you must, of course, use the recommended face/eye shield.

You can quite happily use an arc welder outside, as long as it's not raining! Apart from this practicality, one of the other big advantages of these machines is their longevity. With just a transformer inside the box there is nothing to go wrong. The Clarke machine here was bought as a secondhand unit but, despite being about six years old and with an unknown history, it's still performing faultlessly.

The basics

Known technically as 'manual metal arc welding', arc welding has been around in various forms since the late 1800s and the basic idea is a simple one. The intense heat generated by an electric arc is used to melt and fuse together pieces of metal so that, when cool, they are joined for good.

The electrical power for the arc can be taken from either a DC or an AC source but it's the latter which is the more commonly used in the motor trade. DC-powered machines require a generator to operate them and are more generally suited to agriculture and other outdoor applications where a mains power supply is unavailable.

The AC machines are actually little more than transformers which ensure that the 240V from the mains is adjusted down to a more usable level. Consequently, there are no moving parts and so reliability, efficiency and portability are all excellent.

Controls are minimal on a modern arc welder – an on/off switch, a current setting wheel and a couple of cable terminals are all you get for your money. Of the cables to be connected, one features a large, spring-loaded clamp, known as the earth or return clamp, while the other boasts an electrode holder.

The knitting needle-like electrodes used in arc welding vary in length and diameter for different applications but the part they play in the whole process is invaluable. The electric arc jumps between the tip of the electrode and the metal surface being welded and is maintained as long as the crucial panel-to-electrode distance is kept correct.

The earth clamp is attached to the workpiece so that when the electrode is brought close to the surface the current jumps the gap (in the form of an arc) to

Arc welding, while not the most controllable or exacting of welding techniques, is a process with plenty of potential for the DIY user. Admittedly it's not in welding's Premier League any more, certainly as far as car body restoration and repair are concerned. The likes of MIG have forced its relegation to the lower divisions but, in terms of affordability and versatility, the humble arc welder is most definitely still a strong First Division player.

These days arc welders at the DIY end of the market are very cheap to buy. For £50, or even less sometimes, you can buy a machine that will have the capability to join most types of metal, permanently. However, the affordability of the machines and the perceived simplicity of their operation rather gives the impression that an arc welder is an easy tool to use. Unfortunately, it is not!

complete the circuit and run to ground. Controlling the arc by the selection of different electrodes and current settings is what good arc welding is all about.

Getting started

Anyone new to this technique would certainly be well advised to practice for a good while on scrap metal before moving on to a proper job. Your first task should be to select the right electrode. This must be matched to the type of metal being welded and most machines are nowadays supplied with a few mild steel electrodes to get you started.

If your overalls don't have a buttoned cuff then tape them up like this to guard against anything nasty creeping up your sleeve.

You will notice that the electrodes are not shiny like metal but have a dull, powdery appearance. This is because they are flux-coated. This coating (commonly a mixture of metal oxides and silica) is added to the metal electrode for a number of very important reasons.

We've already established that the electric arc melts the metal being welded but it also consumes the electrode as it does so. The electrode's metal core is melted into the 'weld pool' beneath the arc to supplement the weld as it progresses. The flux coating is also melted and, under such severe conditions, it combines to form a 'slag' which rises to the surface of the still molten weld to form a protective layer over it during cooling (see Fig.1). You see, molten metal is very vulnerable

to oxidation and contamination from the atmosphere so it's important for the overall strength of the weld that this sort of protection is provided.

The diameter of the electrode is another important factor. Any measurement of this you see printed (1.6mm, 2.0mm, 2.5mm etc.) refers to the diameter of the metal core of the electrode, not to the overall diameter including the flux coating as well. Don't get confused by this. Different diameters should be used for welding different thicknesses of metal (as you might have imagined) and some instruction booklets do include suggested thickness/diameter tables to help you. If not, the best thing is to consult your local welding supplier who, once he knows the type and thickness of metal being welded, should be able to advise.

It's very important while you're getting the welder set up that it remains switched off. Unlike a modern MIG unit which has a non-live torch controlled by a trigger, an 'arc' has no such refinement and the electrode holder remains live all the time the machine is switched on.

The one control you can play with on an arc welder governs the current. This is a very important factor because it establishes the power of the arc which, in turn, affects its performance. The current setting must relate to both electrode diameter and the thickness of the metal being welded. Once again, most decent machines these days are provided with guidance about this but, of course, this is only a guide. Every situation is different so experimentation is the key to establishing control settings.

The final aspect of preparing to weld involves attaching the earth clamp. This must be fastened to the workpiece (before switching on) close to the welding area and it's important that the contact between it and the metal surface is good. Therefore, old paint, rust, dirt, wax and grease should all be removed if needs be to ensure this.

The average arc welder is a simple device with few controls. An on/off switch, a current control wheel and a couple of cable terminals are all there is.

A pair of decent leather gloves is another safety essential. Those with elasticated wrist bands like this are ideal.

Finally, it's worth mentioning protective clothing. Arc welding is a potentially dangerous process so you must take sensible precautions. A face shield with suitable filter to protect your eyes is essential. A good pair of close-weave cotton overalls is also to be recommended together with decent leather gloves, preferably with elasticated wrist protectors. The last thing you want is sparks and molten globules of metal dropping down your sleeve or inside your glove!

Striking the arc

There are two ways to start or 'strike' the arc. Both involve bringing the electrode tip down momentarily into contact with the metal surface but one employs a tapping action while the other uses more of a scratching motion, like striking a match (see Fig. 2).

Striking the arc for the first time with a new electrode can be difficult because the flux coating often extends over the end. Once you have done it, though, restarting should normally be less of a problem although, if you leave a half-used electrode for some time this may be difficult to re-start unless you grind off the tip until you see shiny metal again. This is worth doing on the more expen-

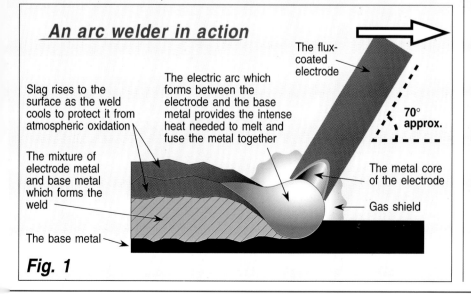

An arc welder in action

Slag rises to the surface as the weld cools to protect it from atmospheric oxidation

The electric arc which forms between the electrode and the base metal provides the intense heat needed to melt and fuse the metal together

The flux-coated electrode

70° approx.

The mixture of electrode metal and base metal which forms the weld

The metal core of the electrode

Gas shield

The base metal

Fig. 1

The ART of ARC

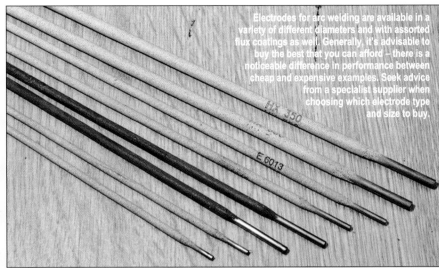

sive rods like those for welding cast iron.

You will find that the ease with which the arc can be struck does vary from electrode to electrode. Some will strike easily while others will require a hard hit before the arc lights. Of course, striking the arc is only half the battle because, once it's going, you then have to maintain it. This involves lifting the electrode to between 3mm and 5mm (even more on heavy gauge metal) above the panel surface so that it continues to jump.

The electrode holder has a spring-loaded lever to clamp the electrode into place. Always make sure that the bared wire end of the electrode is gripped in the holder to ensure a good contact. Most holders allow the electrode to be fixed at two or three different angles, the choice between these depending on personal preference.

Your ability to retain this electrode-to-metal gap is crucial to the overall quality of the weld being produced. The problem is that it's made doubly hard by the fact that the electrode is being consumed by the arc which means that as well as having to guide the electrode along the joint being welded, you are also having to lower it to match the rate at which it's being used up.

If you hold the electrode too close to the surface then it is likely to become welded to it. This will be a very common occurrence for the beginner and the best thing to do when it happens is to release the spring grip and pull away the electrode holder to break the circuit, leaving the electrode 'stuck' in place. Do this as soon as you can because the longer you leave the current running the hotter everything will get. If the whole electrode gets over-heated then the flux coating may well crack and start to flake off, in which case it will have to be scrapped. If it's not visibly damaged after disconnection, then break it off the panel with a pair of pliers or by hand wearing gloves.

If the electrode is held closer to the panel surface than it should be, but just too far away actually to stick, then the arc will not be producing sufficient heat to create a good weld. The weld bead will sit proud on the surface as though it's just been laid down and there will be no penetration to speak of. If, on the other hand, the electrode gap is made too large then the arc will spread, excessive spatter will be produced and, again, there will be virtually no penetration. Also the flux has a tendency to roll under the weld bead and get trapped under these conditions. If you lift it still further away then the arc will simply stop.

More problems!

As if all this wasn't enough, you also have the speed of the electrode's movement and the current setting to worry about. I've already touched on the latter and, really, this is a matter for trial and error (probably plenty of both!). However, as a guide, the tell-tale sign of a unnecessarily high current setting is excessive hole-blowing. The problem comes, especially if you're new to the game, in deciding whether it's the current causing the problem or one of the other variables which you have got wrong!

The speed with which you move the electrode along the joint is also of vital importance in the overall scheme of things. Needless to say, this has to be just right if the weld produced is to possess all the right qualities. If you progress too quickly then you will end up with a thin ribbon-like bead, or even intermittent blobs, on the surface with no penetration at all.

Moving the electrode too slowly is likely to blow holes although, if the current is also set too low for the thickness of metal being welded, you will get excessive flux in the weld pool. This causes problems when you come to remove the slag because it won't chip away as easily as it should. In extreme cases it can turn globular which makes it virtually impossible to remove and weakens the strength of the weld into the bargain.

The most straightforward arc welding technique, and the one which all beginners should master first, is called 'downhand' welding. The electrode is moved from right to left (assuming you are right-handed) along the joint and held at an angle of about 70° in the direction of travel.

The right angle

The way in which the electrode is held, as well how it's moved, is of great relevance here. This angle of 70° is an im-

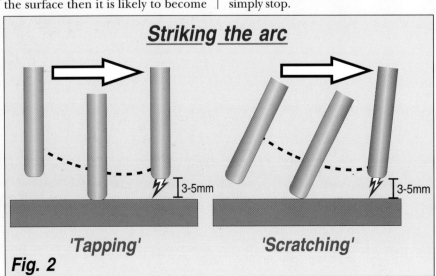

Striking the arc

'Tapping'

3-5mm

'Scratching'

3-5mm

Fig. 2

portant one to remember because it has a marked influence on the weld itself. Holding the electrode at too shallow an angle to the surface being welded will lead to the arc spreading out to the sides and this will diminish its effect. Consequently, any resultant weld will lack penetration. Alternatively, if you position the electrode too vertically, in relation to the metal surface, the likely outcome is that penetration will be excessive and holes will be blown.

Additionally, if holes are not blown (because the current is too low, perhaps) the steepness of the electrode's angle will mean that the flux will tend to drop directly into the weld pool and so the process still won't be as effective as it should be.

It's also important that the electrode is angled towards the direction of travel. This will help the flow of the flux as the weld progresses. If you try to weld in the opposite direction, the flux tends to get put down ahead of the weld which is not good.

Working with this 'downhand' style is the most effective and easiest way to use an arc welder. It ensures good penetration, assuming your technique and control settings are correct, and is the most comfortable method too. There are, of course, times when it's just not possible to weld like this. You may have to work

Ideally, if an arc weld is just right then the slag layer on top should start to peel away as it cools. In most cases, though, it will require some gentle persuasion using a small hammer or similar. Wear goggles to protect you eyes when attempting this.

on a vertical joint or even overhead and both are a good deal more awkward.

The welding of a vertical joint can be done in either an upward or a downward direction, the choice really depends upon the thickness of the metal involved. If it's thin then working from top to bottom is the best approach, with the electrode angled slightly (10-15°) back from the direction of travel. Doing it like this will minimise the risk of blowing holes. On thicker metal (5mm and over) vertical welds should be tackled from the bottom, often with a slight weaving action (with a small triangular

motion) as well. This will ensure the high degree of penetration needed to make the weld secure.

Overhead arc welding is the hardest of the lot and it's not something that we would recommend to anyone but the most experienced user. There is a big danger from falling slag and molten metal and it's very hard to get the weld even because working in this way is so awkward.

A final word

From what you've just read it should now be clear that arc welding is a difficult and demanding technique to master. It'll take plenty of practice before you develop any proficiency so try not to be disappointed if things don't go smoothly at the start. Striking and maintaining the arc so that a weld run may be completed is an art in itself, to say nothing of setting the current and choosing the correct electrode! What I've covered here has just scratched the surface really but it should be sufficient to get you up and running.

In many ways arc welding is much harder than MIG which, I suppose, goes some way to explaining the yawning gap in popularity between the two!

My thanks to Tony Fairweather for his kind help with the preparation of this feature.

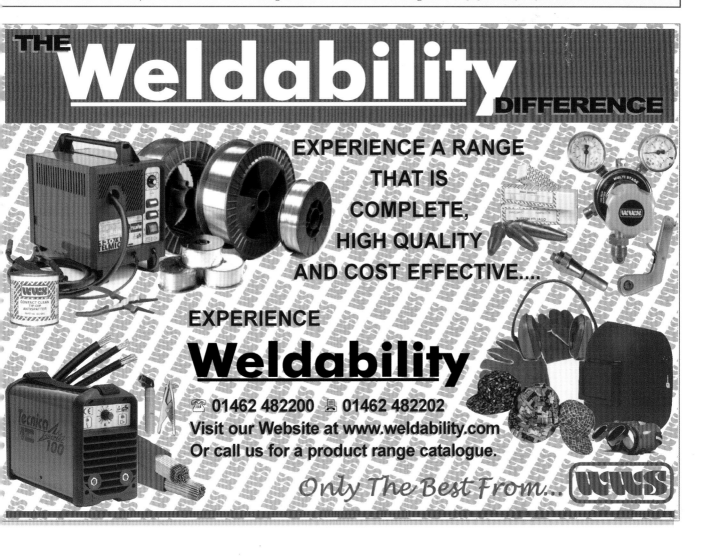

Welcome to the *Car Mechanics* Start Welding Supplement!

As you can see, the supplement is divided into five sections. We start with general techniques, a feature which explains, in clear, simple, and easy-to-follow terms, what MIG welding is and how actually to start joining bits of metal using your bright, new just-out-of-the-box welder.

This is by Chris Graham who, as well as being a regular *Car Mechanics* contributor, is one of Britain's leading experts on automotive welding techniques - MIG in particular. He's written many definitive features on the subject and has just published his first book.

We then go on to cover four typical welding repair jobs – wings, rear valance, floorpan repair sections and sills. These are the most commonly-needed structural/rust repairs and, once you've learnt the basics, any of these jobs can be tackled using a decent DIY-quality MIG welder.

We've tried to use examples which are as complicated as possible. The floorpan repair involves fitting a panel under the rear bulkhead, the wing job a lot of inner wing work and repairs to the wing itself and the rear valance some back-end damage.

We haven't done this to put you off, it's to make the features cover as many problems you MAY come across as possible. If your front wing job's as bad as our Alfa's you're very unlucky, however, it's unlikely that your jobs will require any techniques we haven't demonstrated on it!

We haven't really set out to show full restoration techniques, where everything is put back exactly as original. Rather, we're demonstrating safe and workmanlike repair methods that are appropriate to the cars we cover. Take floorpans for example. Someone doing a full restoration would make the joint between old and new metal completely invisible at the very least.

But while that's quite appropriate and correct for, say, a classic Jaguar, it's completely pointless on a £350 Montego! The technique shown is a cost-effective repair and fine, as long as the welding's satisfactory and the repaired metal is as strong as the original – which means continuous welding all round if you're using two or more bits to do something originally done by one.

Of course no written material, however comprehensive and well-written, can teach you how to weld any more than Manuel in Fawlty Towers could learn English from a book. It takes practice – usually quite a lot of it too – before you're ready to move from joining bits of scrap metal to joining bits on to a car, and then it takes even more practice before you're really proficient.

It's well worth persisting though, because once mastered (and anyone with sufficient patience can do it), welding is a skill which you'll never lose. It'll stay with you for ever! Go on - give it a try!

Peter Simpson Editor

CONTENTS

Starting with a MIG
51

Rear valance replacement
54

Repairing & replacing sills & wheelarches
58

Repairing and replacing inner & outer front wings
62

Repairing floorpans
66

PLEASE REFER TO PAGE 109 FOR SPECIALIST WELDING ADVERTISERS

MIG WELDING

Chris Graham outlines the rudiments of setting-up and using a MIG welder for the first time.

Few would argue with the benefits of MIG welding. Machines are widely available nowadays and the process itself is quick, safe and relatively simple. The smallest sets are very affordable and even the cheapest are capable of professional-quality welds, such is the general quality today.

Machines can be bought in most DIY superstores and starter kits normally come complete with everything you need to start welding – face mask, shielding gas, filler wire, spare contact tips etc.

The technique itself is very effective and extremely versatile – plus points which account for the MIG's almost universal popularity throughout the motor trade today. However, you do have to learn how to use a MIG welder – it isn't impossibly difficult but there is a certain knack which has to be practised on pieces of scrap steel before you go anywhere near a car.

Why MIG?

All types of welding use intense heat to melt or fuse together the pieces of metal being joined. On a MIG an electric arc generates this heat. The arc is produced by a transformer/rectifier set-up within the main body of the machine.

The welder's casing also contains a spool of filler wire. Variable control motorised rollers drive this from the reel up an armoured cable to the trigger-operated torch or handset. It passes right through this and emerges, via the contact tip, out through the nozzle.

Current is passed up the filler wire so that, when the torch nozzle is brought close to the subject metal and the trigger is pulled, an electric arc jumps from the tip of the wire down on to the metal. During this process the filler wire melts and

Fig. 1

Droplets of molten filler wire falling within the arc

Inert gas shielding the weld as it forms

Weld pool

falls into the joint to provide extra strength. This is why it is fed continuously to the torch. Feed rate is variable.

MIG stands for 'metal inert gas' which gives a clue to the other vital function performed by the torch apart from providing the filler wire and current. It also delivers an 'umbrella' of

1 Tacking a joint before it's welded is vital for this sort of repair work. Note the spacing between tacks and the earth clamp in the foreground – clipped on to clean, bare metal to ensure a good connection.

MIG WELDING

inert shielding gas around the weld as it forms (see Fig. 1). This gas is very unreactive and its job is to ensure that the newly-formed, molten weld is protected from atmospheric contamination. Naturally occurring oxygen, nitrogen and hydrogen can all have a detrimental effect if they come into contact with the hot weld. It is very important that the gas shield remains complete but, unfortunately, there are many factors which can affect it.

The shielding gas, normally carbon dioxide, is contained in a mini canister strapped to the back of the MIG's casing. There are alternative gases which can be used, or even mixtures of gases, but these are for more specific welding applications and need not concern us here.

WHEN MIG WELDING...

- Always use eye/face protection
- Always wear full length gauntlets
- Always work in a well-ventilated area
- Always keep children/pets well away
- Always clean off old oil/paint etc
- Never look directly at the arc
- Never weld near fuel tank/pipes
- Never weld overhead if inexperienced

The filler wire comes in different varieties too. The important thing to remember is that its type must be matched to the metal being welded. Generally it is assumed that most enthusiasts will be using their MIGs for working on mild steel for which copper-coated mild steel filler wire is standard. Wire diameter varies as well, with the choice here relating to the thickness of the metal being welded – 0.6mm is ideal for car bodywork thickness steel so this is what's normally included in the kit.

Virtually all modern MIG machines feature a 'non-live' torch – until the trigger is pulled, nothing happens. Switching on starts the gas and current flowing and activates the wire feed mechanism.

The electric arc forms between the filler wire tip and the metal subject to complete an electrical circuit. For this to happen the workpiece must be earthed using the welder's return lead and clamp. If the clamp is not connected to clean, bare metal the arc will not jump.

The finer points

Good MIG welding is a balancing act with probably the most important factor being the stability of the arc itself.

Without a stable arc, consistent welding, good penetration and therefore strength, are impossible. Factors which affect the arc directly include torch-to-metal distance, voltage setting, wire speed setting, angle of the torch and the speed at which the torch is moved along the joint. All are inter-related and a full understanding of how each affects the other only really comes with experience.

The secret of good MIG welding is reacting to the changing performance of the arc. This is what makes it such a hard subject to describe fully in a feature like this. There is just no substitute for practice, practice and more practice. Only with trial and error will you start to appreciate the control you can develop over every aspect of the process.

First time they use a MIG, almost everyone blows holes in the metal! The cause is overheating which melts the metal completely. It can happen in a fraction of a second which makes it very hard to predict. The primary causes of overheating/hole blowing are having the voltage setting too high (there are usually between three and six settings on most small units) or moving the torch too slowly.

Think of the voltage setting as controlling the power of the torch. If you have it set too high then it will simply blow the metal away. Similarly, if you progress along the joint too slowly you will induce more heat than the metal can stand.

Ideally the arc should emit a continuous crackle as you weld, often likened to bacon frying in a pan. The sound of the arc provides another tell-tale sign as to welding efficiency. Noticeable fizzing and popping, for example, indicates that the voltage has been set too low, not too high as you might imagine.

The best advice for beginners is to start with a low voltage setting and work up until the arc becomes stabilised. This assumes, of course, that you have developed the ability to maintain the torch's height and speed of movement correctly.

With the torch held too far away from the surface either the

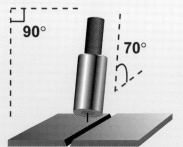

Correct torch angles

90°

70°

Torch should make an angle of about 70° as the weld is made, but be maintained vertically from side to side.

Fig. 2

arc will be very spluttery or it will not form at all. Move in too close, however, and the risk is that you will overheat the head of the torch and possibly damage the contact tip.

Practice makes...

Start by setting up the MIG with a medium wire speed and lowish voltage selection (the instruction booklet should provide basic setting-up details) and then concentrate on becoming proficient at depositing runs of weld in a controlled manner. Initially you will find it hard even to keep the arc going, let alone avoid burning holes. The weld 'bead' will twist and turn as you struggle to see

2 This is the sort of mess that most beginners churn out to start with. Blown holes, an uneven bead, poor penetration etc. The heat-affected zone is clearly visible here.

what's going on through the heavily-tinted eye protector which must always be used.

In time, though, your skill will develop. Keep stopping to inspect the bead's appearance as this can tell you much about your technique, or lack of it! (see Fig. 3).

You will soon discover how fine the torch height tolerance is. Try to keep it at 2-3mm. Maintaining this consistently is hard enough when the torch is held in one place but doing so while moving it along a joint is doubly difficult. But you'll get used to it!

One further complication is that the torch has to be angled away from the vertical in the direction of the joint but kept upright in the opposite plane (see Fig. 2). Maintaining an angle of about 70° along the joint plane ensures good coverage from the shielding gas. If you tilt any more than this, gas concentration is reduced, leading to problems with weld contamination and, ultimately, weakness.

Keeping the torch at 90° to the metal will help to promote good penetration and an equal effect on both sides of the joint. Angling to one side or the other will direct too much weld off centre which can be another cause of joint weakness.

All this can seem pretty well impossible at first, especially with such restricted vision. Until your eyes get used to concentrating on the arc – quite safe through a proper mask/filter – you will find it hard.

Angle of view is important. Don't be afraid to put your head down close to the arc (use a professional-type hinged head shield if possible) to make things as clear as possible.

Position yourself low and to one side of the arc so that you get a good view. Holding your head directly above is hopeless because you will be too far away to see what's going on and the arc will probably be

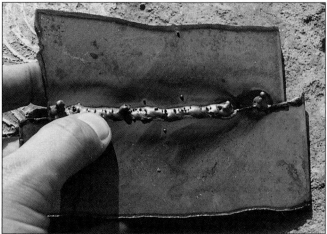

3 A clear case of weld contamination causing porosity – tiny holes in the bead. This severely weakens a weld and is usually caused by problems with the shielding gas supply. Is the cylinder empty or is it just poor technique?

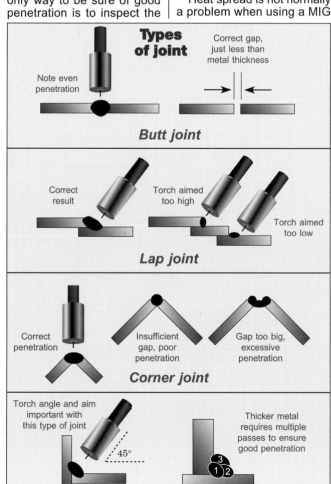

Thin and rounded	Correct bead	Too wide and flat
This narrow bead results from a 'short arc' caused by high wire speed and/or low voltage	The bead as it should be with good even penetration and oval cross section	This flat, wide bead is produced by a 'long' arc, caused by low wire speed and/or high voltage

Typical bead shapes
Fig. 3

obscured by the torch nozzle.

Looking closely you will be able to see the arc plus an area of molten metal immediately beneath it – known as the weld pool. The prime objective is to maintain the arc consistently so that, as the torch is moved slowly, it pushes this molten pool along in the desired direction.

I mentioned earlier that speed of torch travel is important. Most beginners tend to move too quickly in their anxiety to avoid blowing holes. This will lead to a thin, stringy weld which, when viewed from the other side, lacks penetration.

Strength in depth

Proper penetration is another key factor – without it a weld will always be sub-standard. The only way to be sure of good penetration is to inspect the weld from the back. If nothing is visible at all, or there is a broken line showing, then the weld is no good.

With reference to Fig. 3, you can see from the 'Correct bead' example in the centre that, for complete penetration, the weld bead must extend right down through the entire thickness of the metal and protrude slightly underneath.

A further useful indicator of weld quality is the 'heat-affected zone'. This is the area of discoloration that forms on either side of the weld as a result of heat spread. When all settings are correct and general technique is good, this area should extend about 10mm on either side of the bead when welding body thickness sheet metal (up to 1mm).

Heat spread is not normally a problem when using a MIG welder, not in the same way as it is with oxy-acetylene equipment. The all-but instantaneous nature of the heat generated by electric arc avoids almost completely the risk of panel distortion. The one time when it can be a worry is during the welding of thicker metal which resists hole-blowing. Without this obvious sign of trouble it is easy to work with the voltage set too high. In such cases watch out for a wide, flattish bead shape – a characteristic indicator.

'Spatter' is another tell-tale sign of excessive voltage setting. If the welding process becomes too violent, droplets from the molten weld pool are whipped up and thrown out on to the surrounding metal where they settle and solidify. This is not a disaster but makes the weld look shabby and can be time-consuming to clean off with a grinder.

Joint effort

There are several types of joint commonly found on automotive applications (see Fig. 4). All can and should be practised on scrap metal before trying them for real.

The butt and lap joints are probably the two most widely used on a motor car and the former is the harder of the two to execute, particularly on thin metal sheet. Because you are joining metal edge-to-edge there is little room for error. Holes are easily blown on body thickness sheet and some of the cheaper MIG units do not have low enough voltage settings to avoid this.

To ensure good penetration on thicker material you must leave a gap between the two pieces – not necessary on thin panel work. Alignment is crucial too. It is essential that any gap left is parallel along the length of the joint.

Sometimes it's possible to clamp the two pieces together with Mole grips etc but for bigger jobs this often isn't practical. The alternative is to tack the joint. Most professionals adopt this technique because there is no chance of any further movement once it is done.

Tacking involves straddling the joint with spots of weld to secure it at regular distances along its length. Spacing is important to counter any tendency for heat-related distortion. When welding body thickness panelwork put a tack every 5-6cm to be safe. On thicker material they can be more widely spaced.

A final useful technique, and one which emphasises the versatility of the MIG, is that of plug welding. In car construction one of the most widely used welds is the spot weld. Two sections are clamped tightly together by electrodes which then pass a current between them to fuse the metal into a circular weld at that point.

You can recreate this original-looking effect with a MIG by pre-drilling the top section of metal, clamping the two together and filling the resultant hole with weld (see below).

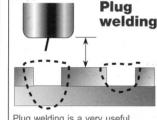

Plug welding

Plug welding is a very useful technique, especially when you are trying to re-create that original 'factory' look. Success will require plenty of practice on scrap metal. Torch height is the all important factor. Too far away from the panel will result in poor penetration (on right) while holding it too close will blow a hole. A good 'plug' will show penetration clearly on the underside (example on left).

Types of joint

Note even penetration

Correct gap, just less than metal thickness

Butt joint

Correct result

Torch aimed too high

Torch aimed too low

Lap joint

Correct penetration

Insufficient gap, poor penetration

Gap too big, excessive penetration

Corner joint

Torch angle and aim important with this type of joint

45°

Thicker metal requires multiple passes to ensure good penetration

T-joint   Fig. 4

TYPICAL PROBLEMS

FAULT	COMMON CAUSES
Arc won't form	Torch too far from surface Earth lead not connected
Arc unstable	Voltage set too low Torch height erratic Shielding gas failure Intermittent wire feed
Poor penetration	Torch moving too fast Voltage too low
Blowing holes	Torch moving too slowly Voltage too high
Weld contamination	Lack of shielding gas Torch at wrong angle Nozzle blocked with spatter

REAR VALANCE SWAP

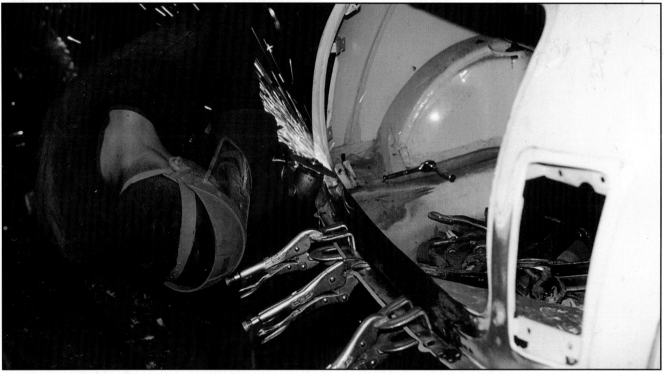

In many ways replacing a rear valance is an ideal first job to tackle with your MIG and using plug-welding techniques.
Taking the ubiquitous Mini as an example,
Pete Wood explains what's involved...

For nearly 40 years, the Mini has provided transport for the masses. The design is simple and luckily, parts are extremely cheap. Why luckily? Well, because the Mini is so small, even a minor bump will usually affect more than one panel.

Our subject was stationary at traffic lights when a larger saloon gave it a gentle rear end tap. The boot lid and lip were creased and the boot floor buckled. To repair the damage properly, a new panel has to be let in below the boot lid – where the hinges, securing the boot lid, are fastened. To gain access to the buckled boot floor, it's necessary to remove and replace the rear valance.

Because this panel is always prone to rotting, especially on older Minis, it makes an ideal case study.

The techniques involved in doing this job on a Mini are remarkably similar to those used on many other vehicles too. For information, we've also covered briefly the back-end straightening technique.

Stripped for action!

When it comes to replacement panels, you have a choice between original equipment and pattern. As regular readers will know already, OE panels are expensive but are usually a better fit. Pattern parts are cheaper but sometimes require more 'fettling' to get a decent fit, though

1 Lights, bumper, fuel tank, and boot lid are removed, labelled and stored. On older cars, it's wise to soak all bolt threads with WD40 or similar.

2 With only light rear end damage to be pulled out, a 'dozer' is used. A steel bar, passing through clamps on the sill, is used as the anchor point...

3 ...while the hydraulic arm pulls chains clamped to the bodywork. The controlled pull is generally done at the same angle as the direction of impact.

4 While the stretched metal is under tension, the floor is beaten with a hammer to restore the general shape. Note the safety rope – in case the chain breaks.

7 The valance is cut up to, but not including, its top lip – where the valance is spot welded to the boot floor and tail panel. Now there's access to...

10 Now there is full access to straighten out the last creases in the un-cut section of the boot lid surround. A thick, blunt chisel makes a crisp edge.

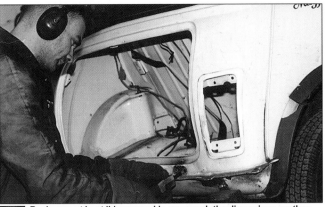

5 Replacement boot lid surround is measured; the dimensions are then transferred to the damaged panel before it's cut out with an ultra fast air saw.

8 ...locate the original spot welds by grinding back the paint – above and below the panel lips. A respiratory mask should be worn when cleaning off paint or filler.

11 Sand down the remaining paint, filler and corrosion in the boot floor before reaching for the hammer and dolly; more preparation – a better final result.

6 Another worthwhile investment is the belt-driven sander/grinder. It's narrower than a disc grinder and is ideal for getting at restricted, rusty bolt heads.

9 Once the spot welds have been drilled out, the panel lip should come away without much difficulty. A bolster chisel will separate any stubborn welds.

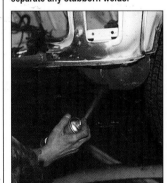

12 Weld through primer is used to keep corrosion at bay. A double coating is applied to the underside which will be boxed in by the rear valance shortly.

aftermarket quality's improved dramatically in recent years.

In the case of our car, which is getting a bit long in the tooth, the insurance assessor stipulated pattern parts to help keep costs down.

The first step with any body repair is to clear as many of the surrounding bolt-on components and accident debris as is possible or feasible. Here, the bumper, rear lights, boot lid, fuel tank and battery are removed – though not before all the mounting bolts were soaked with penetrating oil.

A note was made of all the small washers, rubbers and trim showing wear or damage when stripped. These were put on order straight away as small

components can take days to source; panels are usually dispatched in hours.

The panels were ordered from Veng. When they arrived, we checked they were damage-free and correct for the year of our car by matching them against the damaged bodywork. This is important as panels can be damaged or wrongly supplied and once you've started fitting them they won't be accepted back for credit.

On a car with a long production run, like this Mini, subtle design changes may mean that the shape of a panel has changed slightly over the years. So always quote the car's chassis number, when ordering, to lessen the risk of a wrong order.

Pull it straight!

It's important to straighten the car before anything's cut out. This is usually done on a jig. However as our Mini has only light damage, a portable, and relatively cheap-to-hire, 'dozer' was used instead.

Two large clamps are bolted to the sills, just rear of the doors. A large, steel tube, running through the clamps, is used as the anchor-point for the dozer.

The golden rule of straightening accident damage is always pull out at the same height and angle as the direction of impact. Because this Mini was hit squarely in the back, a straight and level pull is required.

Hydraulic pressure is exerted a little at a time, so the whole operation is always fully controlled. While the bodywork's under tension, the panel beater uses a hammer on the raised sections of the bruised metal to ease the boot floor back into shape.

Old valance off!

Once the car is generally straight, we can disassemble the car in the same way as it was constructed – drilling out the spot welds on the panel lips. Life is much easier if you have plenty of access to wield the drill.

An air saw is a great help (though certainly not essential)

REAR VALANCE SWAP

when it comes to cutting away old steel, leaving only the spot-welded, panel lips. Check constantly that the saw is cutting only the old panels and not any hidden brackets.

You can now find the original spot welds by grinding off the paint along the panel lips, revealing the weld depressions. Use the specially designed, hardened spot-weld twist which is almost flat at the cutting end. Professionals use a drill, where the depth of the spot weld twist can be pre-set so it cuts through the top layer of metal, only. If you're using an ordinary electric drill, go slowly and gently to minimise damage to the panel below the welds.

The old panel lip will often pull away quite easily although sometimes you'll need to part stubborn welds with a bolster chisel. The remaining damage to the boot floor was rectified with the traditional dolly and

hammer once all the paint was sanded away. The naked steel was protected with weld-through primer.

The boot lid surround was offered up and the excess metal trimmed with an air saw so that there was only 1-2mm gap between the panels – for a neat, butt weld. This panel was held in place with plenty of Mole grips and welding clamps. It took some time to get everything square. Even with a bit of filing, it's always a compromise.

The boot was fastened temporarily to make sure it sat squarely and then removed.

are spot welded. If you don't own the necessary equipment, a MIG welder will do the same job although it takes a little longer. Starting from the centre of the panel, working outwards, each hole is plugged with puddles of MIG weld which are ground flat when cool. Plug welds cut down on distortion, compared to a long run of MIG, because the heat is localised. Any minor distortion is dressed flat with the hammer and dolly.

The rear valance is held with Mole grips and plug welded along its length. As you can see by the photos, the pattern

13 New boot lid surround is clamped into position, then trimmed to size. True welding clamps are useful but expensive – Mole grips will suffice on open areas

14 The hinge is added for stability and to check that the boot lines up after the initial tacks are made. Close tolerances save time and cut down on distortion.

15 When using pattern parts, the panel gaps will often need adjustment. Here a run of weld is used to give the top lip a little more 'body'.

16 Once the weld is ground down and panel beaten, the repair is almost invisible. Only a thin skim of filler is required to take up any slight discrepancies.

17 The valance is now clamped on. Holes are drilled through each outer panel lip, every 1-2in. Removing paint helps to let the MIG run smoothly, but...

18 ...factory primer is so thin that when these plug welds are made, the MIG can cope. Note how the weld fills up the drill hole and overflows – a substitute spot weld.

19 Now the valance is firmly welded, the difference in width can be clearly seen. The excess steel is ground back to match the dimensions of the back panel.

The hinges were left in place to give more support to the adjacent panel while the initial tacks are made. We'd noticed that there was quite a large gap between the left-hand, lower edge of the boot and its surround. This was overcome with a bead of weld on the top lip of the replacement panel. This was later ground to shape.

The hinges were now removed and the boot lid surround butt welded. The weld was dressed with a grinding disc until it was flush with the panel, giving an almost invisible repair.

Holes are now drilled into the bottom lip of the boot lid surround – not into the boot floor beneath it. The hole spacing is roughly equal to that found on the original panel – about every 2in. At the factory, the panels

valance overlapped the boot lid surround and boot floor panels by 0.5in, or more, in places. Five minutes' work with a grinding wheel soon sorted that little problem...

Sealant is applied around the seams of the valance to keep water and muck from creeping inside the box section. If the owner has any sense, Waxoyl should be sprayed inside as further protection.

The paint around the surrounding repair area is feathered back and a thin skim of filler applied to smooth out any discrepancies. A few layers of paint and no one will know that the Mini was ever in a scrape.

Our thanks to accident repair specialist, DeeJays of Essex (Tel: 01992 451595).

20 Yes, you did do a good job. Now go and get some filler and paint to finish it. And you will spray some rustproofer into that box section, won't you?

SEALEY POWER WELDERS

PORTABLE AND PROFESSIONAL MIG WELDERS

150 AMP PROFESSIONAL MIG WELDER

- ✓ Proven wire feed system for trouble free welding.
- ✓ Model No. Supermig 150/5
- ✓ List Price £373.75

SPECIAL PRICE £299.00

185 AMP PROFESSIONAL MIG WELDER

- ✓ Professional contour grip, quick release Euro Torch.
- ✓ Fitted with spot weld timer
- ✓ Model No. Supermig 185
- ✓ List Price £586.25

SPECIAL PRICE £469.00

210 AMP PROFESSIONAL MIG WELDER

- ✓ Excellent continuous performance on car panel thickness material.
- ✓ Model No. Supermig 210/10
- ✓ List Price £748.75

SPECIAL PRICE £599.00

250 AMP PROFESSIONAL MIG WELDER

- ✓ Extra large chassis takes full size gas bottles.
- ✓ Model No. Supermig 250/10
- ✓ List Price £873.75

SPECIAL PRICE £699.00

130 AMP MIG WELDER

- ✓ Forced Air Cooling System for high performance.
- ✓ 130Amp Max Power Output.
- ✓ Ergonomically designed handle with non-live torch.
- ✓ Gas and wire included.
- ✓ Model No. PM130XT
- ✓ List Price £323.75

SPECIAL PRICE £259.00

150 AMP MIG WELDER

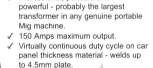

- ✓ Professional, portable and powerful - probably the largest transformer in any genuine portable Mig machine.
- ✓ 150 Amps maximum output.
- ✓ Virtually continuous duty cycle on car panel thickness material - welds up to 4.5mm plate.
- ✓ Model No. PM150XT
- ✓ List Price £348.75

SPECIAL PRICE £279.00

210 AMP MIG WELDER

TURBO COOLED

- ✓ Turbo fan cooled.
- ✓ Huge COPPER WOUND transformer.
- ✓ Unbeatable spec at this price - 210 Amps max, 160 Amp at 20% and 200 Amps at 16%.
- ✓ Fantastic duty cycle.
- ✓ Euro quick release torch.
- ✓ Model No. Automig 210
- ✓ List Price £723.75

SPECIAL PRICE £579.00

250 AMP MIG WELDER

TURBO COOLED

- ✓ Electronic Autospeed wire feed control device with fused protection.
- ✓ 7 level rotary power control selection.
- ✓ Model No. Automig 250
- ✓ List Price £873.75

SPECIAL PRICE £699.00

SILLS & ARCHES

Jim Patten explains the right way of welding new sills. It's not as hard as you might think – even if, as is usual, part of the rear wheelarch needs doing too...

This Rover 216 had not impressed the MoT examiner. He sent the car away with a stern warning not to return until new sills had been fitted. As is so often the case, though, the rust had spread to the wheelarch as well as the inner sill, making proper rectification a little more complicated. However, this is quite typical of what the job usually involves – most cars are constructed and rust in basically similar ways, so the techniques shown here can be considered pretty universal.

Before we begin, though, a few words about general preparation. The job was done outside, away from any combustible materials but protected from the wind. To retain as much rigidity within the shell, one side was tackled at a time. The car was raised and set on two stout axle stands. It is essential that the area to be cut and welded is completely cleared of trim and other combustible materials – watch out too for hidden wiring and fuel lines!

1 A first cut with the angle grinder has been made along the top of the sill to be trimmed further as required later. This was followed at the bottom using a sharp steel chisel close to the spot-welds.

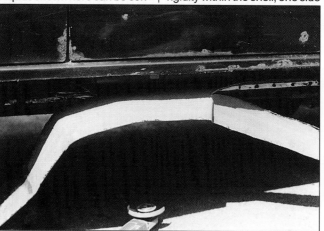

2 Most of the sill has been cut away here although it was still necessary to trim the top edge still further to beyond the first fold. This was then tapped down slightly to facilitate a lap-weld. The steel chisel dealt with the lower spot-welds before being cleaned up with a coarse sanding disc.

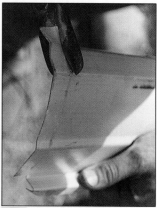

3 Most aftermarket (and not a few OE...) panels need a little fettling. Offered up against the car it proved to be too long and needed trimming. Good, sharp snips made a clean cut without causing distortion.

36

4 Rarely does the inner sill escape from rot as can be seen here. At least the basic shape was intact and could be used to form a template from cardboard. The rust was cut away until good, sound metal was found.

6 A block of wood was used to support the sill while holes were drilled along its length at the same distance apart as the spot-welds of the manufacturer. These would provide the basis of the circular welds later.

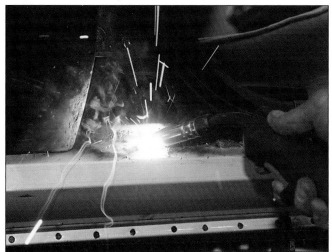

8 Continuous welds are made along the top sill edge are made after tack welds had secured it in place. We strongly recommend having someone to 'fire watch' with a fire extinguisher just in case.

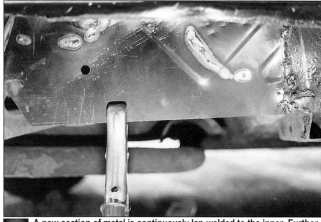

5 A new section of metal is continuously lap-welded to the inner. Further welding is been carried out from behind where a box section abuts against the inner sill. Weld is just visible on repair section showing good penetration.

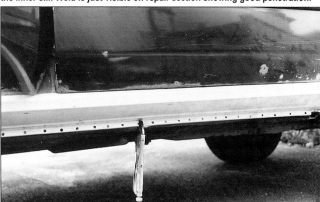

7 A trial-fit of the new sill shows that the door is still a bit tight along the edge. The remnants of the old sill were still a little to high and needed tapping down to get the gap right. Several trial fits are normally needed.

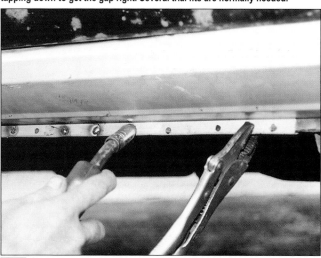

9 Simulating a spot-weld is not as easy as it looks. Practice is needed to get this technique right. The weld starts inside the hole and circulates out to attach the sill. Once mastered, though, the technique is straightforward.

The first cut

Using a steel cutting wheel on an angle grinder and a sharp steel chisel, the main body of the sill was cut away leaving a strip along the bottom spot-welded edges behind and a lip at the top step to form a base for a lap weld with the new sill. At the front (adjacent to the wing) a straight vertical cut made the separation from the front wing, leaving a fine strip of sill left to weld the new panel to. The bottom spot welds were then attacked with the chisel although, where the metal was weak, a coarse sanding disc on the angle grinder simply ground the old metal off. A spot-weld drill bit would do the job well enough but this would make a hole all through and we need the parent metal as a base for the new sill.

All traces of the old metal must be removed to ensure a flush fit for the new panel and this was taken down with a coarse sanding disc with the edges straightened with a panel beating hammer and dolly. Although decaying in a big way, the remnants of the wheelarch are left in place for now to help position the new sill.

When offered in place, the new sill should butt against the front wing with the top leading edge over as far as possible. You may need to tap the remains of the old sill step down a little to get the new sill to fit. Closing the door with the sill held loosely in place will determine the sill to door gap. At this stage, getting the correct length was important. Using Mole grips to hold the sill in place, its position is checked before making a mark to correspond with the wheelarch. A further double check was made before removing the sill to trim the end. Only use the very best of metal shears on this edge. Old and blunt ones will turn the metal edges and the shape of the sill will distort.

Drill holes were made along the bottom flanged edge. When this is welded in place, each hole will be filled with weld, making a permanent bond to the car, replicating the original spot weld. The inner sill was sound enough although, just after the rear arch, rot had taken a hold

SILLS & ARCHES

but was confined to a rectangular section. Rust was cut away using a combination of steel cutters and the angle grinder until good solid metal was left. Then the area was made good, ready for welding.

Using cardboard as a template, the area needing repair was traced over the cardboard. This was then cut to size and offered back on the car. Some trimming was needed for a perfect fit and then the template was transferred to a sheet of 20 gauge steel. A little extra was left over when the steel was cut out and trimmed to fit as required.

The welding begins

When an area of rot is replaced by a repair panel, then that panel should be fitted using a continuous weld to retain original strength. Where spot-welds were originally used, then that's how the repair should be made with the same spacing distance. It is also important that the same gauge of steel is used. We used an SIP Topmig 170 amp MIG-Welder using argon gas. Smaller home MIGs will work fine but argon is always the best gas medium.

Our newly-cut repair panel was laid in place on the inner sill and held on one corner by Mole grips. The earth lead was clamped to a clean part of metal close to where the weld would be. Tacks were made at each corner to secure the metal. The Mole grips could now be released. To avoid distortion, short weld runs were made at opposing sides of the repair; eventually they all joined together forming a continuous weld.

With a coarse sanding disc on the angle grinder, any excess weld is taken down so that the new sill will sit flush. At last the sill could be offered in place. Several sets of Mole grips are now required to hold it on firmly. If you don't have so many grips, small 'G' clamps may serve. Another look around

10 The wheelarch just fell apart on one side making it awkward to get the sill positioning right. As the other side was still intact, measurements were taken from it and transposed over for an exact fit.

11 Continuous welding is needed everywhere that new metal has been let-in – you're making two bits do the job of one after all! Here the bottom of the wheelarch is welded to the sill in an over-lap weld as per the original.

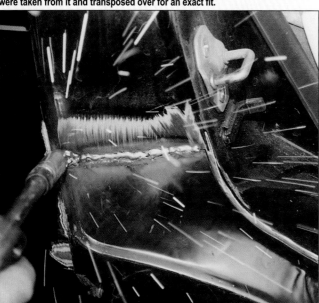

12 Sparks fly as the top part of the wheelarch is welded in. Because there was no need to go beyond this seam the repair section was trimmed to fit. This was a butt-weld where two sections meet exactly head on. Great accuracy is needed when fitting panels in this way.

13 Not all the rusty area can be accommodated by one repair section. A hole has been cut in part of the wheelarch and card is being used as a template for new metal. After trial fitting, the cardboard's dimensions will be transferred to the metal.

14 That's the sill end panel going in. The welding has yet to be finished and cleaned up. On this side a lot of chasing was necessary to find solid metal as the rust had penetrated quite a way up the inner wheelarch.

15 A coarse sanding disc on the angle grinder is used to remove the excess weld build-up. It is possible to be to heavy handed with the grinder and this will seriously weaken the area.

16 See how the door gap has been retained around the wheelarch and sill. If attention is not paid to this area, the door may rub when it is closed. The gap, of course, must be established before any welding takes place.

17 Proud sections can be tapped down lightly to make the area flush. Better to do this and retain the integrity of the weld than have ground off too much metal. Go easy though or you will make a lot of extra work for yourself.

18 Production paper on a rubber block is used to flatten off the body filler. The grades used become finer. Work until sanding marks are no longer visible.

19 After priming, Stone-Guard is sprayed on. Masking tape is applied to about three quarters of the way up the sill because from there on up, just paint is required.

20 Black Smoothrite was found to be a close match to original. It will serve until a full respray is done. Inside, Waxoyl was used to protect the cavity.

the job to make sure that it is all flush and still fits before the welder is picked up. A few tack welds are placed first just to hold the sill in place and then yet another check is made. This time the door is closed to make sure that the bottom gap is good and that the sill is to the right contour.

Establishing all to be well, continuous welding of the top could begin – again in short runs until they all merged together. The join here would be a lap-weld as the new sill fits over the remains of the old. A panel beating hammer is kept nearby to tap down the sill to fit where necessary. Even with localised heat, the sill will still spread. In an ideal world, the replacement sill would fit on to the existing spot-welds but this would involve getting in to the A & B posts and is not really practical. Anyway, the replacement sills are made to fit on a lap basis.

Moving down to the lower edge, another Mole grip is brought into play. This is kept near each of the previously drilled holes to get the sill as close to the inner sill as possible. It was found that the lower edge of the sill was actually below that of the inner and constantly needed lifting. A broad edge chisel finally tapped it home.

With the MIG wire starting on the inner sill at the centre of the hole, a circular 'whirlpool' type motion makes the two metals whole. It's important that the sill be held firmly in place, otherwise the heat would lift the sill away from the inner and, although it would hold, there would be a gap between the two. At the front, the sill is carefully welded in the vertical to the remains of the old sill.

Underneath the arches

Only the lower part of the repair section is needed so it was trimmed to suit. Then holding it against the car as a template, a mark was made on the wing. The old arch could finally be cut away. Because a butt weld would be needed, the cutting away of the old metal had to be extremely accurate and there could be no open spaces between old and new metal. There was more rot inside the inner wing but it was only a 'bit lacey' at the bottom. At this stage, it only needed cutting out; the repair would come later.

Loosely holding the arch repair, the door was closed to make sure that the gap was good. Once confirmed, Mole grips held the section in place while a tack weld offered a more permanent grip. The door was closed once more and the gap re-confirmed. Now the continuous welding could begin on the basis of short runs. As ever, the earth clamp is located as close

to the work as possible.

Now the hole at the end of the sill in the inner wing could be plugged. Once more a piece of cardboard was used as a template and transferred over to the 20 gauge steel. Due to the location of the repair, it is slightly more difficult to hold in place but a combination of clamp and wedging worked in the end.

A bit of decorating

To finish the job ready for painting, a coarse sanding disc was used to grind back the welds and generally tidy up the area. Be careful if you do this at home. You could get carried away and grind through the welds. You need to get them almost flush with the parent metal and it is better to leave a bit extra than grind through. Any proud areas were tapped in slightly and a thin spatula full of body filler applied. This was rubbed down using a rubber hand block with production paper (a non-clogging type of paper). Gradually finer grades were used until there were no

sanding marks at all. A quality primer was sprayed over the area first, followed by stone chip for the lower three-quarters of the sill.

When this had hardened, black Hammerite Smoothrite was used as the car was to be resprayed at a later date. It turned out to be a fairly good match actually.

TOOLS NEEDED

MIG welder of at least 100 amp output using argon gas.

Angle grinder with steel cutting wheel and coarse sanding discs

Sharp broad-bladed chisel

At least five Mole grips

Electric drill and bits

Metal cutters

Large and panel beating hammers

Stout axle stands

Masking tape

Rubber sanding block

FRONT WINGS

Fitting the replacement wing. The front end is tacked first. After all the cut lines have been lap welded the wing is plug welded to the A post.

Pete Wood explains how to weld front wings on, and how to repair the old wing if replacements are expensive.

Old Alfas aren't exactly common. Those beautiful Italian lines cover a multitude of mud traps which, when corrosion does get a hold, make the car depreciate faster than the Lire.

A few surface blisters in the top of the driver's wing were the only clues that something was amiss. The owner wanted to replace the wing but, when he found out that factory replacements only were available, decided to follow a more economical route.

The plan was to cut off the wing, let in a repair patch and ascertain how much corrosion had taken place in the inner wing. Quite sensible really; any rot in the outer wing is normally a sure sign that there's worse underneath.

Although the job's shown being done on a relatively rare Alfa, the techniques that follow are pretty much universal (fitting one wing's very much like fitting another) and can be applied to virtually any car. The inner wing repairs are also fairly typical. However, ready-made repair sections are available for common vehicles that rot here – though localised rot is still often best repaired using home-made sections. The wing repair techniques are mainly for information – unless, of course

1 First job is to drill out the old spot welds. When the wing flange is as rotten as this one it doesn't take long using a spot weld remover or even a twist drill.

2 Note how the cut runs adjacent to the original factory weld so this is preserved at the finish. Wing corrosion can be seen very clearly as well.

3 When you can't get at the spot welds by conventional means, a bolster or air-driven chisel eats through steel very quickly – but go carefully!

4 The lower part of the wing was cut just above, and parallel to, the sill. And because it's flat, blending in the repair is easier.

5 Once more, the cut at the front end is made slightly to one side of the original weld line for an invisible repair – forward planning.

6 Even from a distance, it's obvious that very little of the outer wing flange is left. What remains is kept for reference purposes.

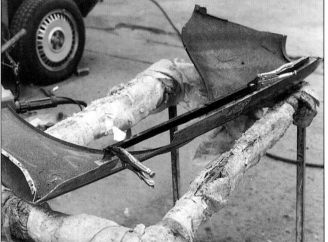

7 The wing is placed on a trestle and a replacement flange is tacked on to the fragile remains of the original. The bad steel is cut off later.

8 With the new flange acting as the datum point, new guttering and a repair section for the top of the wing is let in.

9 The outer wing is completed but this is all that's left of the inner wing to weld on to. A cardboard template allows us...

10 ...to make the first of three repair sections forming the flitch plate. Because the metal is so thin, the power to the MIG is turned down.

you, too, have a car for which replacement panels are expensive or unobtainable.

Wing removal

It was obvious from the start that this would be no easy job. All the bolts securing the trim were rusted solid. Many hours were spent on grinding and drilling.

The wing was cut just below the windscreen, above the sill, and next to the original welded line – where the wing joins the

front end of the car. An air saw makes a thin, neat cut.

The bonnet and door have to come off – to get a drill on to the spot welds. Not that there were many left.

It was difficult to get at some of the spot welds to the rear of the wing. A bit of brute force from an air chisel and the wing peeled away from the A post in seconds.

When the paint was stripped from the outer wing the corrosion was fairly extensive. Most of the securing flange was rot-

ten and someone had replaced a fair amount of steel with chicken wire and pudding. Hence the bubbling.

The decayed flange was cut away, leaving a little at each end of the wing as a datum point. It's all too easy to cut out too much at once, then weld in great lengths of fresh steel and find that nothing lines up when the wing goes back on. It's far better to weld in small sections a little at a time so that you, the welder, are in control – not the elements.

Scrap metal flange

The replacement flange was cut from scrap metal. Once the flange was tacked into place, the rain channel section of the wing was let in. Then the rotted outer section of the wing was repaired with more scrap offcuts. Apart from a bit of cosmetic work, that's the outer wing finished.

So far, so good. We knew the inner wing wouldn't be so simple. Not only was the inner flange non-existent but the flitch

START WELDING SUPPLEMENT – Front Wings

FRONT WINGS

panel was badly corroded – probably as a result of a previous repair which we subsequently found.

A cardboard template was made, measurements taken from the old flitch panel, and its shape transferred to 18 gauge steel. Three repair sections were made to keep distortion to a minimum. These sections were tack welded into place, clamped against the strongest parts of the old, inner wing to keep the lines true. The hammer and dolly were used frequently to overcome heat buckles. Each repair section was made slightly longer than needed so that each piece overlapped when welded. Looks aren't important here; the flitch panel will be hidden by the outer wing.

A piece of Dexion was perfect for making a replacement inner wing flange. This was welded, in one long hit, to the refurbished flitch panel. When it was ground down the repair looked as good as it was strong.

Fitting the wing

The outer wing was tacked to the front end first. This is most important – as anyone who has gone to look at a secondhand car will know. Most of us automatically look at the shut lines between the wing and bonnet as well as looking at the wing to valance lines – to see if the car has had major repairs. Get the front end right and the rest of the repair will almost take care of itself.

We expected the back of the outer wing to be out a little at the back end. And it was. However, a steel wing has a little 'give' so, when we pressed down on the top of the structurally sound panel, the cut lines were close enough to get some tacks on to them.

The flanges were drilled and plug welded because no spot welding equipment was to hand. The back of the wing was rejoined to the A post in the same manner. All four cut lines were

11 After every welding step is completed, the plate is made square with a hammer and dolly to preserve the flange reference line.

12 Each repair section overlaps the next and is butt welded for extra strength. Not particularly pretty but here strength is more important. It took 30 minutes to reach this stage.

lap welded and ground down.

Primer and paint was applied quickly and flexible wax-based undersealant was then brushed on over the top for further protection against rust.

The total cost of consumables and scrap metal came to less than £20 and took around ten hours to complete. That's a big saving over the £450 quoted by one body shop. And another pretty car is saved from the breaker's yard...

Our thanks to Bollingmore of Twickenham (Tel: 0181 977 7799).

13 The inner flange is made from scrap Dexion and lines up perfectly with the refurbished flitch panel. Note the window cover...

14 ...which prevents molten metal from getting embedded into the glass. The inner wing is now strong enough to stand on.

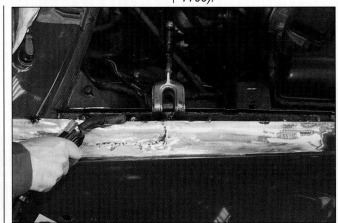

15 Holes are drilled into the outer flange every 2in and plug welded. Clamp stays one hole ahead to prevent wing movement. Attach to A post as shown in heading shot.

FLOOR PANS

Using his recently-acquired Montego as an example, Jim Patten explains how to make and weld in an effective floor/boot repair panel – a welded repair that's often needed on other models too.

When the back seat on our Montego was lifted for cleaning, a most horrid sight lingered beneath. Corrosion had taken a firm hold on the floorpan and had even spread into the boot area. The reason became clear as traces of water were found nearby and, following the trail, a faulty rear screen rubber looked the likely root cause. If you ever come across of water finding its way into a car, cure it immediately or suffer the consequences.

Repair panels are not available to suit every need and so a certain amount of creativity is sometimes needed. Whatever method is chosen, it will never be quite the same as that used by the manufacturers. This particular panel is one large pressing with its ends buried deep in the car's inner structure. The best we can do, short of taking the whole shell apart and start-

1 Always remove anything inflammable before welding. The seat base came out by lifting and pulling but the backrest was secured by screws, two 8mm at the bottom and another accessed inside the boot holding the top of the seat.

2 Plastic side trims cover some rust and will also succumb to heat generated by welding. They, and the draught excluders, must be removed. This one is held by screws and trim clips. Alas, the clips broke and required replacing.

3 Just visible here are the top flats of the box section (it's actually a top hat type of construction) that is spot-welded to the floor pan. Another outrigger runs off from the side, revealed when the floor was peeled away.

4 Lots of sound deadening is used on some parts of the boot floor. This must be removed otherwise the heat will cause it to melt, resulting in unpleasant gases rising and causing irritation. A screwdriver is usually enough to dislodge them in their solid state.

5 Using a coarse disc and an angle grinder will give you a good idea on how far the rust has spread. What looked like a good painted surface actually contained plenty of rust holes (some quite big), all of which came to light following a good going-over with the grinder.

6 Here the seat support panel has been lifted to allow a piece of cardboard to slide beneath to be used as a template. The extent of the repair needed is marked and a slight overlap made before the template is cut to size.

7 When the template's been cut to size, the various bends are marked. It helps to make a note of which way they are to be bent because, when the template has been removed, it can be a bit confusing. It's not that unusual to bend the metal in completely the wrong direction. With an assistant (me actually!) holding down on the template, a mark is made from beneath the car to identify the box sections. This will be needed later when the floor is welded to the box section flats.

8 The rusted sections can now be cut out using a cutting wheel in an angle grinder. Aff is using an air-driven cutter here. It is possible to use a cold chisel but it does make mess, distorting the metal and making uneven cuts. Great care must be taken when cutting near the box sections. The cutter should be used lightly from above until almost through the metal and finished with the cold chisel, otherwise the box sections may be damaged.

9 This is where the cold chisel is needed. Spot-welds are broken through where the floor meets the box section. A good chisel should get through each weld with a blow or two. If it doesn't, continued hammering will cause distortion – get a sharper chisel.

10 Box section flats must be as clean and smooth as possible to ensure a perfect weld. The angle grinder takes away the remains of the old spot-welds and prepares the area for welding. The welds broke cleanly and the box section remained straight.

11 Our template is now transferred to 20 gauge sheet steel. There was just enough to get the required shape. Aff used an air cutter to cut the metal. You can use tin-snips but only quality items – poor snips will bend the metal before cutting it.

ing again, is to cut out the infected area and weld in a new section.

Aftermarket panels are designed to fit this very need but, in the case of our Montego, these aren't available. What looked to be extremely depressing actually turned out to be fair-ly straightforward and proved a decent repair. Although we are covering the Rover Montego here, the model's almost irrelevant as the technique is applicable to just about any make of car you can think of.

The floor pan had corroded above a chassis member but luckily the rot had not damaged the box section. Spot-welds secure the floor metal to the box section and so this would have to be replicated on the repair. Initially, it was thought that two repairs would have to be made, one beneath the seat and the other in the boot. However, the seat backrest support had also corroded where it met the floor pan, enabling a full repair section to be passed beneath, joining the two together. The original panel was one pressing anyway.

First the area would have to be cleaned up to assess the

FLOOR PANS

amount of rot and then a cardboard template made to get the correct size and shape of metal. Various bends would be needed and these, too, would be highlighted on the template. This would include the flats on the box section, essential for accurate positioning of the

welds from floor pan to box section. Rainham Road Car Care had the job and their Aff Gohar (who, as we've seen in the X1/9 project, is pretty good at welding and fabrication) did the welding. Our picture/caption sequences gives a step by step guide as to what was involved.

Protection

Once that the job had been finished, we decided to leave the welds rather than grind them back. You can't hide repairs like this and at least the quality of welding is evident. As a further precaution, Waxoyl was sprayed into the box section just in case rust had started. At least this would prevent it from taken a hold and develop into true corrosion. Undersealant was applied to the underside as a protection against the elements and road debris.

A couple of things to consider with this type of repair. On the lower side of the floor pan most manufacturers apply an undersealant coating. The welding heat will cause this to melt and, if in direct line, it will burn. This

12 Aff doesn't use fancy tools for bending metal – all you need is a couple of pieces of stout angle iron. Marks from the template have been transferred over and the metal is tapped back to the correct angle. Of course this can only be guessed at this stage so a number of trial fits may be needed.

13 Marks had been made on the template of where the box sections are and this has been transferred across to the metal. Holes are now drilled to facilitate the spot-weld. The rust is simply on the surface where the metal has been stored. It cleans off easily with a wire brush.

18 To complete the repair, an angle piece is welded from the seat support to the new floor. This is simply a piece of steel bent to the rough angle and tweeked until it fitted perfectly. Continuous welding was applied to every edge.

14 Although the new repair section has been bent to suit, it will also need to be hammered in place. This hammer contains shot inside a plastic head and does not leave such a mark on impact as a conventional hammer does. These holes must be flush with the box section to get a good weld.

15 It may be necessary to hold the edge of the metal down when applying a tack weld Here a screwdriver pushes the metal home. Use of a hammer will flatten the surrounding metal for a flush fit.

19 The completed job. See how the new panel extends beneath the seat support to the affected area in the boot. Where spot-welds had originally been, there are now spot MIG welds. This is now as strong as the original one-piece panel.

burning will be localised but great care must be taken not to allow it to ignite anything else. Always have an assistant to keep an eye on this.

Check out where the fuel tank and lines run too. Had this corrosion been on the other side of our Montego, then the tank would have had to come out. I remember vividly when a friend was welding a Volvo 340 chassis member. Volvo had chosen to run the fuel line inside the main chassis rail. Of course the heat melted the plastic fuel line and the fuel ignited. He was very extremely lucky avoid a serious fire. NEVER underestimate how easily a fire can start.

Needless to say, the rear screen rubber was filled with a screen leak repair solution and we will be keeping an eye out for further water ingress.

Our thanks to Aff Gohar and Rainham Road Car Care (0181 592 3887) for their help with this feature.

16 A circular weld is applied through the previously drilled holes to join the floor pan to the box section beneath. The two have to be absolutely flush to make a permanent repair. Weld tops can be ground off but this isn't essential.

17 See how the floor pan repair has been bent to join the inner sill. Tack welds have been strategically placed followed by continuous welding. Occasionally, the repair panel has to be tapped flush with the inner sill. Note also that, although the wiring loom was taped back with masking tape, it was accidentally nudged and fell back towards the work. Watch out for potential problems like this.

20 All that's left now is to give the repair some protection for the future. Jenolite Double Act primer is painted over any bare metal surface. To make the job complete, it could be painted with top coat too. Beneath the car, a liberal dose of Waxoyl over the Double Act is advisable for protection against water.

WELDING for the MoT

By Jim Punter.

There is currently a lot of mystery surrounding welding repairs for the MoT test. It all starts with deciding what causes a failure in the first place and, if something does fail because the metal is either broken or excessively corroded, then can it be weld repaired and what level of welded repair would be good enough for the MoT and how should the job be done?

First it is worth a short recap on the most likely reasons for failure from corroded (mainly rusty), broken or damaged metal. The problem will initially concern either the structure of the car, or the bodywork. Let's have a look at the bodywork first.

The front valance on this Metro has to be replaced. The new panel is the same design as the original and spot welding is acceptable.

Bodywork Repairs:

The only MoT criteria for the condition of a vehicle's bodywork is whether or not the damaged or corroded areas are *'likely to cause injury'*. In practice the situation is as simple as that and it is up to the MoT tester to decide in any given instance.

So if an accident has resulted in a jagged edge of torn metal projecting out which a pedestrian or cyclist could injure themselves on, then that will result in a failure. On the other hand, if an accident has only resulted in a dented door for example and there are no sharp or jagged edges sticking out in such a way as to be likely to cause injury, then that would be acceptable for the MoT.

It is worth noting that the problems caused by corrosion are not quite the same as those caused by accident damage. It can be quite difficult to effect an

acceptable temporary repair if an accident has resulted in a jagged piece of metal sticking out. Normally replacement of the panel would be the only real answer. On the other hand if corrosion has resulted in a sort of 'knife edge' on the side of a wing, for example, then this can be sorted out very effectively by covering the area with heavy woven 'cloth' type adhesive tape to remove the danger of injury from somebody brushing against the corroded area. These types of repair are quite acceptable provided the likelihood of injury is completely removed.

Missing Bumper End Caps:

The definition of 'bodywork' extends to the bumpers as well as the wings, doors and so on, and in practice a lot of MoT failures result from damaged bumpers. The most common problem arises from missing bumper end caps which leaves the sharp edge of the central bumper blade projecting out to the side. Although it is theoretically possible to

cover these in heavy woven industrial tape to render them safe and so acceptable for the test, in practice the cost of replacement end caps is quite low and they are very easy to install.

Welded Bodywork Repairs:

Sometimes a simple 'patchwork' welding job on damaged bodywork may be the best way of effecting a repair for the MoT should the cost of replacing a panel be unacceptable. Unlike structural 'patch' repairs, seam welding is not needed here. Simply tacking a repair plate in place will be perfectly acceptable (in fact pop riveting would also be good enough), but remember that welding can leave jagged 'splatter' so make sure the surface is ground smooth or properly filled before taking the car to be tested. However, these days with modestly- priced panels available it is not likely to be worth the trouble to do such temporary repairs for the MoT. The only situation I can envisage is if a replacement panel is unavailable.

Structural Repairs:

Within the MoT regulations there are various ways in which a car can fail the test because of structural damage or corrosion. However, when it comes to repairing the structure for the MoT, it is vital to bear in mind that :-
any failure which results from structural damage or corrosion must be repaired so that replacement metal of the correct thickness is properly welded in place so that the repaired

component is at least as strong as the original to fully remedy the problem, and in some cases welding repairs are not allowed at all unless agreed by the vehicle manufacturer.

In practical terms this means that the following factors have to be taken into account:

Allowed Repairs: Is the damaged or corroded component one which can be repaired for MoT purposes or is a replacement the only acceptable remedy?
Metal Thickness: Is the metal used to effect a repair of adequate thickness?
Welding Quality: Is the welding up to the required standard for a repair of the item in question?
Area Being Repaired: Does the repair cover a wide enough area to make sure that the new metal is welded to parts of the original structure which are not damaged or corroded?

Let's have a look at each of these in turn:

Allowed Repairs:

The testers' manual states:-
"Welded repairs to highly stressed components such as suspension arms etc. are not normally acceptable. If in doubt consult the vehicle or components manufacturer."

This is not a very useful statement. It is just not practical for either the testing station or the motorist to enter into a dialogue with manufacturers about these details, so ultimately it is a matter for interpretation at the testing station concerned. We take the view that this is probably referring to things like track control arms, suspension pans and so on, and do not accept welded repairs to these items. The best bet is to check with your testing station first if you think the damaged item you want to weld falls into the forbidden category of a "highly stressed component...."

Metal Thickness:

The simple answer here is that the metal should be the same thickness as the original part of the chassis or structure being repaired and generally that is the case, but in practice it is not always absolutely necessary. Certainly if the corrosion is so severe that part of a chassis member (for example) has completely rotted away, then yes the repair metal will need to be at least as thick as the original.

Now imagine that the corrosion is confined to small holes in a concentrated area but which do not cover the whole of the metal in question. An inner sill with very localised 'pepperpot' rust holes would be a good example. In that case most of the original metal still survives and a thinner plate welded over the top of the metal without cutting out all the corroded area would be good enough.

A problem arises though when the tester examines the repair. Unless he remembers the car and is aware that the thinner plate is to reinforce a weakened structure effectively rather than replace a fully corroded area, then he may decide that the repair has not been carried out to the required standard. So it is better to play safe and use metal which is at least as thick as the original when doing welded structural repairs for the MoT.

Welding Quality:

It is vital to make sure that any panels or repair patches are *properly* welded into place. The weld must have fully penetrated both the new metal and the vehicle structure to which it is being welded.

MoT SILL REPLACEMENT

1. This Vauxhall Nova failed the MoT because of excessive corrosion on the near side outer sill. The worst area being just ahead of the rear wheelarch as shown.

2. The replacement sill is not of the same design as the original. The top only goes into the first crease of the door step. We always seam weld along this join in these instances.

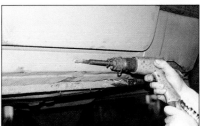

3. When using 'pattern' oversills it is not necessary to remove the old sill along the line of its join to the new one. Cutting beneath the stop not only retains the original shape of the pressing but also provides strong metal to which the new sill can be welded.

4. For any welding job thorough preparation is essential. All corrosion and paint must be removed down to thick bare metal. A small angle head grinder is ideal for this job. Make sure you use protective goggles.

5. To make sure the sill fits properly when the welding is completed it is best to tack weld it into place first. This avoids distortion.

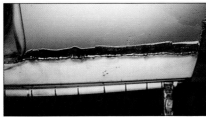

6. Seam welding the upper part of the sill first ensure that the sill does not stand proud and foul the door.

7. To ensure the sill fits correctly at the bottom, use a small jack to adjust the height before welding. On some shapes of sill a strip of wood above the jack is helpful. Note the ground slots in the bottom of the sill to enable it to be welded in place with short strips of weld.

8. The completed job masked up and ready for finishing.

9. In this case the customer has requested a simple spray undersealant finish. If a spray finish is required, then the appropriate preparation and finishing would follow.

WELDING
for the MoT

A weld that is too 'thin' and is just a bead along the joint, not fully penetrating both layers of metal, will result in a failure. Also a join may look as if it has been firmly welded but sometimes there can be too much 'splatter' or oxide around the weld so that the plates are only connected by the flux or splatter; that, too, will be rejected.

To prevent these problems is in most cases a matter of thoroughly preparing the surfaces and using the welding machine at the correct setting and having the requisite skill in its use.

Normally this is not a problem and, in most instances, the metal concerned is not very thick and a good weld is not difficult to achieve with the simplest of welding equipment provided the surfaces are properly prepared. However, in some cases, and the Ford Fiesta rear spring mounting plates are a good example, the components which are welded together are not only thicker than the normal chassis or structural areas but are also subjected to stress loading. In that case very high quality welding is absolutely essential.

The weld must be continuous and *fully* penetrate both pieces of metal being joined. With the thicker metal usually found in these areas it is much less likely that the weld fully penetrates when using the comparatively light duty welding equipment available to the average DIY mechanic. In these instances it may be better to get the welding itself done professionally using heavy duty welding equipment.

Seam welding, spot welding or stitch welding: Now this is perhaps the most difficult area when it comes to structural welding repairs. When motor cars are manufactured most of the welds are spot welded using special robot machines and, if a component is replaced and attached along an original spot welded seam, then spot welding is quite acceptable provided it is up to the same standard as the original...and this is not as simple as it seems.

The original spot weld is quite large and *fully penetrates* both layers of metal. On the other hand the spot welding facility available on small DIY welding machines may not produce a weld of sufficient quality to make sure that the strength of the weld is as good as the original. The answer is to stitch weld the panel into place with a number of short seam welds each about 2cm long with an equal gap between of about the same length.

At our MoT station we have quite heavy duty welding machines but, even then, on the lower part of sills which were originally spot welded we grind a short vertical slot and weld along it to make sure that the weld has fully penetrated and is as good as the original deep spot weld.

In some cases only a seam welded repair will be good enough for the MoT test. If the corrosion is in part of the structure which originally had not been welded at all, and is repaired with a patch, then *seam welding is essential*. It may also be necessary to seam weld a panel in place even though the original was spot welded. This is because some of the replacement panels available as 'pattern' parts which are not supplied by the manufacturer are not of the same

Sometimes two adjacent plates will be needed to repair large areas which are also curved as shown here on the inner flitch of a Vauxhall Chevette. The corrosion here was behind the battery which has been removed. Seam welding is essential here. Part of the welding has yet to be completed.

Rust damage which leaves sharp knife edges would result in a failure. Covering the damaged area with thick adhesive tape as shown here is not a repair recommended by *Car Mechanics* as a proper solution but in fact, as the MoT presently stands, will be acceptable.

design as the 'original equipment'.

Door sills are a good example of this problem. The original sill invariably extends to the top of the door step and is spot welded to the vertical inner sill where the step joins that inner sill. The pattern parts may only extend to the first crease in the door step itself, so theoretically they will have to be seam welded because where they are attached to the structure there was originally no join.

In practice it is up to the MoT tester to decide in these instances and, provided the panel is securely stitch welded in place, then we would be unlikely to fail it. But be warned, because this is a matter of interpreting the rules. The moral is obvious – *when in doubt – seam weld it !*

Size of repair plate

Time and again when we are doing welding repairs for customers we find that what seems to be a relatively small corrosion problem when the vehicle fails the test seems to 'grow' as the metal is prepared either by cutting away with a chisel or, for smaller areas, grinding the surface with an angle head grinder. The reason for this is that corrosion often starts from the inside, and metal that seems solid when seen from the outside is really only very thin and fragile.

The best bet is to tap the whole area quite sharply and vigorously *at the beginning of the job* – you may be surprised at how much rust and corroded metal falls away! Remember it is essential that on patch repairs the repair plate *fully* covers the damaged or corroded areas and is properly welded to a part of the structure that is not corroded or damaged in any way.

So what this all amounts to is that the apparently simple welding job to get the car through the MoT may turn out to be not so simple after all. Make sure that MoT welding job is done properly, it could save a lot of time.

Quick check list

The following check list should provide a useful quick guide:-

1. Where and what is the problem, will it be necessary to replace a panel or will a patch repair be good enough? Perhaps weld repairs are not allowed on that component anyway. Check with the MoT station first.
2. Will seam welding be needed or will stitch welding be sufficient. If in doubt – seam weld.
3. If repairing with a patch make the patch large enough to cover the affected area so that it is welded on to good solid surrounding metal. Here seam welding is essential.
4. Make sure that the thickness of metal used for effecting a patch repair is sufficient to make the repair at least as strong as the original. If in doubt use metal of the same thickness as the original panel or beam.
5. If welding thick components which are subjected to stress loading, make sure the weld really does penetrate both layers of metal and, if in doubt, have it done professionally.

Finally, if you are contemplating carrying out your own welding repair and are not sure of the situation, then have a word with the staff at the testing station, I feel sure they will be only too pleased to advise.

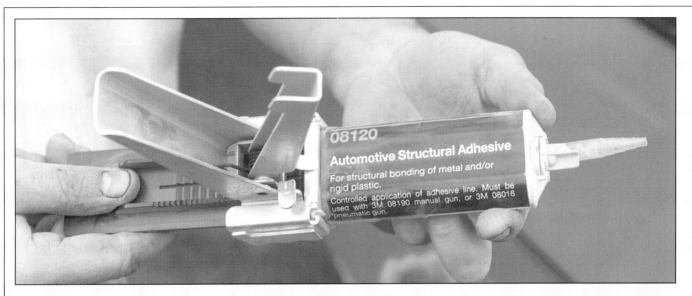

This is a
STICK
UP

Has welding had its day? Jim Patten finds out.

It was an enthusiastic Gary Davis at Davna Speed Cars telling of how a bonded wheel arch repair could be so strong that grown men were able to lift the car from that corner. Of course we had heard of a two pack mixture made by that well respected company 3M but come on lads, we're talking reality here. Anxious to see for ourselves we made a point of being in Dagenham the next time Gary had a job on.

The adhesive comes in a twin pack tube and needs to be applied using a special gun. A tube with a built in spiral mixer is attached to the tube nozzle and as the adhesives are forced out the chemical union begins. Gary would only consider using the adhesive on semi structural areas such as wheel arches and shudders at the thought of anyone attempting to repair something like a suspension top plate.

1. Trim off any rusty metal and thoroughly clean the surrounding area. It will be necessary to remove the paint for a few inches around the arch for making good later.

2. Make sure that the repair panel actually fits. This one needed some trimming along its length.

3. Apply adhesive to the edge of the inner and outer wheel arch. If there is not enough metal then cut a strip to fit and bond in place.

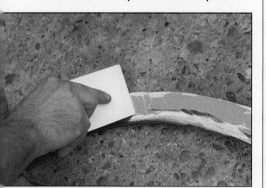

4. With all the paint stripped from the inner side of the repair panel, apply the adhesive and spread evenly with a spatula.

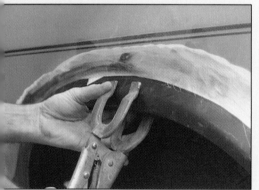

5. Offer the repair panel into place and secure with panel grips.

6. The arch will need to be clamped in several places, so you might have to ask your in-laws, neighbours or any passers-by for a loan of their clamps. If all your favours are used up, try G-clamps. Leave to marinate overnight.

7. Next morning you will have to grind any excess adhesive from the distortion free join.

8. To achieve a perfect blend, use body filler to cover the join. This guy is a master and did the whole run on one scoop.

We tried to pull the wheel arch off and either this stuff works or we're a bunch of whimps. No, dear hopeful, it will not replace welding yet, but it is treading that road. The advantages are clear – all hazards associated with any form of welding are removed – it is quick and strong – the work is clean and distortion free and of course can be done at home with minimal equipment. We are even told that the repair is MoT friendly. The gun is a once-only purchase for around £15 with the adhesive costing about the same and is available from all good car body supply outlets. One tube is really

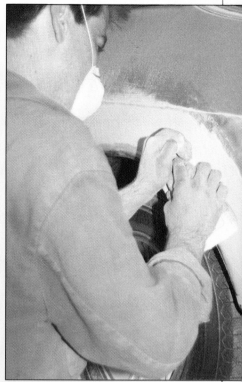

9. Using a block with 80 grade production paper, flatten the area in the usual way, finishing off with a finer grade.

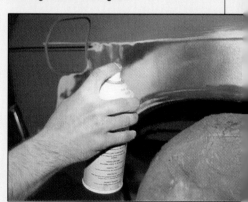

10. Mask up the wheel and any other areas that need protection and apply the primer base.

11. After priming and flattening with wet & dry paper the top coat can be applied to finish the job. Oh, don't forget to smother the back with something like Waxoyl or you will be doing the same job in a year or so.

only enough to cope with one wheel arch so be prepared to spend over £50 including VAT to do both sides. Our thanks go to Gary Davis and Dave Lowe at Davna Speed Cars (081-592 0358) for broadening our horizons.

METAL
MANAGEMENT

Chris Graham kicks off a new welding series, in association with The Colchester Institute, with a summary of the most popular techniques and their applications

MIG is the most popular welding choice today. Full protection for the operator is essential.

Despite what your friendly 'armchair expert' may tell you, welding metal is not an easy business. There are no short cuts to be taken and welding, as with any of the other workshop 'arts' – panel beating, spraying etc – can only be mastered after long hours of practice, patient understanding and enthusiatic application.

Without wishing to put you off straight away, it is vital to appreciate the magnitude of the task. It sounds simple, joining pieces of metal using heat to melt them and, in theory, I suppose it is. But in practice it's far from it. As we'll see during this series there are many subleties to be understood. Each branch of welding has its individual techniques and variations of approach.

Back to basics

Metal welding relies on the harnessing of a concentrated heat source which is used to melt and fuse together the subject pieces. In most cases additional metal, in the form of filler wire or rods, is required to ensure the ultimate strength of the joint. This is added by hand in the gas, TIG and arc processes but automatically with MIG.

Controlling the heat source correctly is fundamental to the process whichever technique you are using. Applying too much heat will blow the metal away while insufficient will create an ineffective joint. Ultimate weld strength relies on complete penetration – the edges of the metal being

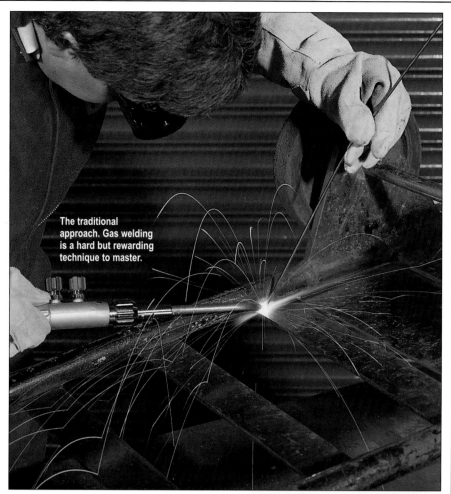

The traditional approach. Gas welding is a hard but rewarding technique to master.

joined must be melted and fused through their entire depth.

Another major factor influencing final weld quality is contamination – the weld 'bead' itself suffers from internal defects limiting its strength. Most commonly this is caused by the process of oxidation leading to porous, brittle and so weakened weld beads. With gas welding the reducing action of the flame guards against this. The more modern MIG and TIG processes employ gas mixtures to shield the newly formed weld from atmospheric gases until it has solidified and the danger period for oxidation has passed.

Impurities in or on the metal being welded will also have a detrimental effect on weld performance. Paint, grease, rust and oil will all upset the process, to say nothing of adding to the fire risk.

For the newcomer, choosing the best method of welding for your needs is a decision which must be influenced by a number of important factors. Cost is perhaps the central issue for most, but frequency and type of use are also very significant.

Probably the least desirable option

Which welds what?

Gas
Will tackle any of the common metals including low carbon steel, galvanised steel, stainless steel, aluminium, brass and copper.

MIG
Will weld mild and stainless steel, spun steel, alloy steels and aluminium. Smallest units do not cope well with thin gauge metal – aluminium a real no-no.

TIG
Can weld everything including alloys, high and medium carbon steel, even titanium.

Spot
Everything apart from aluminium which, because of the oxide layer, is difficult with cheaper machines.

for car repair work is arc welding. It really is a crude process by modern standards and is very difficult when applied to car bodywork. While the units are certainly extremely cheap to buy, their usefulness really is confined to

METAL MANAGEMENT

heavy-duty jobs on thick metal.

The other options all have their plus and minus points which are summarised in the accompanying sections here. We've also considered comparative prices and touched on the vital area of safety. Next month we'll start in earnest with an in-depth look at all aspects of MIG welding.

MIG

FOR	AGAINST
Affordable	Assessing results
Portable	Potential dangers
Versatile	Cheap units overheat

MIG is the most heavily-marketed and accessible modern form of welding. There are many equipment suppliers fighting in a price-conscious market, so discounting and special offers make shopping around well worthwhile.

Quality varies enormously but, as usual, is essentially linked to cost. Bigger, more expensive machines will always perform better so always buy the best you can afford. All are classified by an amp rating. Starter machines are usually around the 100A mark, while semi-professional/professional kits start at 160A.

Entry level machines provide great value and will work 'out of the box', but remember that they are built on a budget and should not be expected to last forever or cope well with heavy usage. Their performance on thin-gauge metal will also often be dubious.

The key to a MIG's performance is arc stability. This is linked to the machine's power – a stable arc requires a beefy transformer and quality electronics to generate it. A weak arc will wander, causing quality and performance problems on thinner material.

The mid-range machines – 150-180-amp – certainly cost more but do a

much better job. The ultimate MIGs are 200+A machines running on a three-phase supply. These are very stable indeed, producing consistently good results, but are well out of the practicality and price stakes for most users.

The MIG process relies on a trigger-controlled handset or torch feeding filler wire, shielding gas and electrical current to the job. A big advantage for the user is that it has a more or less one-handed operation. Operating the trigger switches everything on and off so controllability levels are good.

It is important to note that when working with aluminium and stainless steel, the filler wire must be matched to the composition of the metal being welded. With steel this is not so important.

One of the fundamental problems with MIG is to know whether or not you have achieved complete penetration. The weld can look great from the top even when penetration is woefully inadequate. Good technique and confidence are essential when the reverse of the weld cannot be inspected – box section welding etc.

Running costs should not be a problem although the small gas canisters supplied with DIY machines represent an expensive, if convenient, way to buy the gas. It is far more economical to rent larger cylinder if you are a regular user – availability is much better with many more outlets now than a few years ago.

TIG

FOR	AGAINST
Neatness	Cost
Consistency	Technical difficulty
Controllability	Gas requirement

This really is the aristocrat of modern welding techniques. Standing for 'tungsten inert gas', the technique is based on MIG. Instead of a torch-fed filler wire, the TIG process makes use of a handset, fitted with a non-consumable tungsten electrode, which creates the arc between its pointed tip and the metal workpiece. The filler wire has to be introduced separately, in a manner akin to oxy-acetylene welding, so TIG is another two-handed operation.

As far as cost is concerned TIG units really are in a different and much higher league than MIG machines. The technology within makes great use of electronic inverters, and it is these

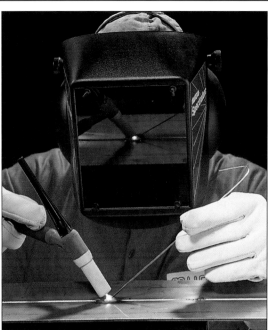

TIG is a cross between MIG and gas welding. It's extremely precise and the first choice of specialist professionals.

Safety First, Always!

Safety is a key issue with any form of welding. All the techniques mentioned here are potentially dangerous so great care must be taken at all times.

expensive components which account for the significant price difference.

The benefit of the electronic wizardry shows itself in controllability terms – far better than a MIG. Bear in mind, however, that the same applies to price as well. The less expensive units, while not cheap by anyone's standards, are certainly not such polished performers as their more pricey alternatives. Once again, you have to pay for quality. Arc quality is again the vital factor and this can only be guaranteed with the top-spec machines.

On the downside, apart from cost, there is no point in hiding from the fact that TIG is a difficult technique to learn. It falls between gas and MIG with regard to the skill and dexterity required, but the results achieved by an experienced user can be superb.

The welds produced are much neater than with MIG and are more like those achievable using gas. You are assured of first class penetration because the focused nature of the arc helps to reduce the unnecessary build-up of filler material.

The secret behind the focused arc is the fact that the tungsten electrode tip is pinpoint sharp. Arc width is governed by electrode width which, with MIG is usually about 1.0mm. Compare this to a finely sharpened TIG tip and you can appreciate the difference. A lot of racing cars and prototype vehicles

MIG/TIG

- Make sure unit's plug and cables are in good order.
- Avoid welding in a wet environment.
- Watch for toxic fumes, particularly in confined spaces.
- Always use a full headshield with correct level of filtration.
- Protect hands and forearms with elbow-length leather gloves.
- Ultraviolet arc light burns exposed skin and damages unprotected eyes.
- Wear clean, close-woven overalls buttoned to the neck.

are TIG welded because the results are so consistent.

Where TIG really leaps ahead of gas is with distortion control. The powerful heating performance of the arc, coupled with its tiny width, ensures that heat spread is minimal, so surrounding panel distortion is rarely a problem.

Gas

FOR	AGAINST
Very versatile	Technically difficult
Neat results	Metal distortion
Controllability	Perceived dangers

Many people rather frown on oxy-acetylene welding nowadays. They worry about managing the 'dangerous' gases and think it less convenient than the more modern, electrical alternatives.

The truth is that dealing with oxygen and acetylene cylinders is no more dangerous than man-handling the propane bottles used in caravan cookers and room heaters. On the versatility front there is nothing to touch it. With gas you can weld, braze, solder, cut metal, use the heat to free seized nuts and bolts, bend heavy gauge metal and even do lead loading.

The welded results are neat and precise, and penetration levels are usually excellent – additional passes can be made with torch only to ensure this. The one potential problem is heat spread. The metal is heated relatively slowly so it spreads and can lead to distortion on thin panelwork.

The supply of the gases is no longer the problem it once was. There are now ample outlets nationwide. In the past, registration as a workshop was required before you could legally use gas welding equipment. These regulations have been relaxed, and your only consideration nowadays need be for your household insurance policy.

Unfortunately, gas welding is one of the hardest techniques to master. MIG is a certainly a lot simpler and more forgiving of the novice too. Gas welding is a two-handed operation which makes it difficult from the start. Operators require good levels of hand/eye co-ordination.

Not only must the torch and filler rod be moved at the right speed, but the rod must be fed into the weld at the correct rate as well. In addition, the balance of the gases is essential too. The proportions of the two may be altered at the torch to achieve different effects for use on varying metal types.

GAS

- Gas torch flame temp. approx. 3,200°C – take care!
- Watch for cylinder gas leaks, especially in confined spaces.
- Always wear correctly filtered goggles, gloves and clean overalls.
- Goggles must be darker when welding with flux – greater flare.
- Avoid inhaling toxic fumes from galvanised/painted metal welding.
- Weld out of doors if worried about fumes.
- Be aware of fire risk at all times – undersealant etc. burns readily.

Completely portable kits are now available – small enough to fit in the boot of a Mini! These are reasonably priced and include everything necessary to get you started – cylinders, hoses, gauges, goggles, regulators and torch. The tremendous advantage of these is their 'weld anywhere' potential.

The only drawback with these small sets is that the tiny cylinders only contain enough gas for about 20 hours of use with a No.1 nozzle. While not a desperate problem, this limitation can prove an irritation for regular users.

Gas cylinders are always rented from the gas supplier because they all have to be tested on a regular basis. The responsibility for this then falls to the supplier not the user.

Spot

FOR	AGAINST
Quick	Capacity limitations
Simple to use	Accessibility
Factory-look	Poor versatility

Spot welding is much more of a specialised application than the others, and yet it is widely used in motor car construction and so is worth consideration here. Spot welding machines are self-contained, electrically powered devices which work simply by heating and compressing.

A pair of copper alloy electrodes are closed to 'pinch' the metal layers being welded. Once tightly shut a current is passed between the two and the resistance it encounters from the steel while travelling from one electrode to the other generates the heat required to melt the metal. The clamping pressure between the electrodes effectively forges the layers into one and the weld is made.

There is no real technique involved, apart from ensuring that the metal to be joined is clean, dry and correctly aligned. Consequently, any sensible person can use a spot welder to good effect. The factor governing effective

The versatility of gas welding equipment allows for a number of other practical uses – not the least of which is cutting.

METAL MANAGEMENT

spot welding is material thickness. Most machines at the budget end of the scale will be limited to maximum joint thicknesses of about 2mm. This is fine for one panel on top of another but any more than this can cause problems.

Trying to spot weld greater thicknesses than the machine can handle will cause the transformer to overheat and its power output will decrease further. The tips will also get extremely hot and become 'mushroomed' which will spread the current and pressure over an even wider area making the problem worse still.

Timers are available as an extra on the cheaper machines (about £60) and are simply used to time the duration of the weld so that consistent results can be achieved. The weld time is determined by trial and error testing – there are no convenient charts available which detail this information.

The electrode tips do become misshapen with use and have to be re-sharpened. Replacements are expensive because they are made of copper/tungsten alloy. The arms, on to which the electrodes are mounted, are expensive too – about £60 a pair. The shape of the arms determines the versatility of the machine.

If originality is important to you and you are after that authentic factory-look then a spot welder is the ideal tool. On the other hand, it is a very limited tool and the results it produces are suited only to specific operations. There are no other uses for a spot welder and so outright purchase is often inappropriate for the DIY enthusiast – hiring usually presents a cost-effective option.

How Much

	DIY	Professional
Gas	£400	£600
MIG	£150	£500+
TIG	£450	£1,300+
Spot	£250	£1,500+

(Guide prices for entry-level equipment)

Spot

- Heat travel limited but burns still possible.
- Wear clear goggles – sparks always a risk.
- Make sure unit's plug and cables are in good order.
- Shield off car interiors where sparks might fly.

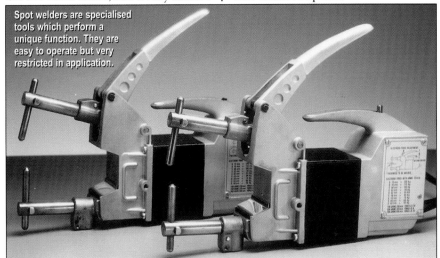

Spot welders are specialised tools which perform a unique function. They are easy to operate but very restricted in application.

It all started with him saying that if those smart-Alecs at Car Mechanics *could do it, so could he...that was 6 months ago... now he just sits in here drinking tea and muttering – "Oh God, Oh God"...*

METAL MANAGEMENT

Part 2: Chris Graham, with expert guidance from vehicle body repair lecturer John Kyle, introduces the basics of MIG welding

Learning to use a MIG welder is rather like getting used to riding a bicycle. It seems impossible at the start but once you can do it you wonder what all the fuss was about.

Cycling requires a certain level of natural balance and co-ordination and the speed of travel is all important. So it is with MIG welding. For successful results the torch must be manoeuvred with controlled skill.

We've covered the detailed ins and outs of MIG welding on a number of occasions already in *Car Mechanics* so the aim here is to provide a practical guide to the 'art' – to answer questions about good technique, setting up the machine and getting started.

MIG or MAG?

It may surprise you to learn that MIG – standing for metal inert gas – is actually an inaccurate term. The name relates to the supposedly inert (unreactive) gas used to provide a protective shield around the weld as it is made. The trouble is that most of the shielding gases used today are far from inert, in fact they are 'active'. Hence the correct reference is MAG. Nevertheless, everyone still popularly refers to the process as 'MIG' and probably will do so for ever more. So will we, at the risk of upsetting the technical sticklers.

At the heart of any MIG welder is a transformer. This converts mains electricity from high voltage/low current to high current/relatively low voltage – a combination more suited to the process.

The other key component within the casing is a wire feed mechanism which pushes a continuous supply of bare metal wire, called filler wire, from its spool up to the torch. On this journey the wire passes through an armoured cable and emerges from the front of the torch having passed through the contact tip and nozzle, sometimes called the shroud.

The all-important current, harnessed to produce the intense heat needed to create the weld, is transferred to the filler wire by the contact tip (see Fig 1). It too is conducted up the cable, as is the supply of shielding gas which is stored in a cylinder usually mounted on the back of the machine. The supply of current, wire and gas is con-

ABOUT COLCHESTER INSTITUTE:

The school of Automobile and General Engineering at Colchester Institute is one of the best known in the country.
This is mostly due to the world-famous vehicle restoration courses, but the school also runs an extensive range of programmes in other areas including vehicle body repair, welding, automobile and general engineering.
For a prospectus call 01206 718000.

TAKE CARE!

The safety precautions required when using a MIG welder cannot be under-estimated.

Of prime importance must be the protection of your eyes. Staring at the naked arc, even for a short time, can induce a very painful condition known as 'arc eye'. The surface of the eye becomes very sensitive and uncomfortable although, in most cases, no permanent damage is done.

Skin is vulnerable too. The ultra-violet light produced by the arc burns like the sun's rays – forearms and necks are often affected. It is all too easy to shelter behind a small, hand-held shield and imagine you are safe. Full-face headshields are the safest option.

Always wear close-woven, cotton-rich overalls. Never choose nylon or any other synthetic material because these will burn and melt onto your skin. Also make sure that overalls are clean – oil or paint-soaked garments are not a good idea. Ideally buttons or poppers should be done up to the neck, and a light material skull cap worn under the headshield to protect the top of the head.

The MIG process does generate sparks and it's important to remember that each one is a globule of molten metal. These will drop down inside an open-necked top or roll up a loose cuff given half a chance – with extremely painful results.

Wear sturdy boots and gloves too, leather if possible. For maximum protection choose elbow-length gauntlets.

trolled by a single trigger on the torch.

Operating this brings everything to life assuming, that is, that the most fundamental step of all has been taken. Every welder features a return lead, often and wrongly referred to as an earth lead. At its end is a large spring-loaded clamp which must be attached to the metal subject being welded. Its

purpose is to complete the electrical circuit and allow the current to flow from the torch to the workpiece and back to the machine.

Current flows down on to the metal being welded in the form of an arc – it jumps the gap between filler wire tip and work piece. The arc is intensely hot and very concentrated. It melts the metal in a flash, causing the edges being joined to flow together and become fused. It is this fusion, or mixing, which gives a weld its surpeme strength.

In addition to melting the work piece, the arc's heat also consumes the filler wire, which is why it needs to be fed continuously up to the torch. A handy consequence of this consumption is that the molten metal produced falls from the tip and is added to the weld. This bolsters overall strength and enhances penetration.

Safe and sound

We've already established that the purpose of the shielding gas is to protect the molten weld as it forms, but from what? Well, the biggest threat comes from oxidation which can lead directly to an undesirable weld defect called porosity – this severely limits overall weld strength.

The idea is that the canopy of shielding gas issuing from the torch nozzle effectively insulates the newly formed weld from all atmospheric gases and thus the risk of oxidation. That's the theory but, of course, in practice things do go wrong.

To ensure an effective gas shield there are a number of important factors to be considered. First, and most obvious, is whether or not there is any gas leaving the nozzle. Failures can be caused by an empty cylinder, incorrectly set regulator or a blocked nozzle.

Gas flow must be sufficient to create the canopy effect. Your machine's instruction booklet will include guidelines on setting the flow rate. The other

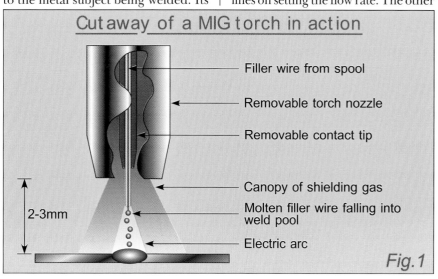

Cutaway of a MIG torch in action

- Filler wire from spool
- Removable torch nozzle
- Removable contact tip
- Canopy of shielding gas
- Molten filler wire falling into weld pool
- Electric arc

2-3mm

Fig.1

METAL MANAGEMENT

major influence is torch angle. Leaning it over too far will allow most of the gas to spill away before it has done its job and weld protection will be poor.

Experts usually advise that the torch is held at an angle of about 70° to the direction of travel, and kept at right angles to the work piece – refer to Figure 2. Unfortunately these requirements are just the first in a series of fundamentals relating to torch operation. All must be observed if good quality, strong welds are to be achieved.

Nozzle-to-work piece distance is crucial. It must be just right for the process to function. Holding the torch too far away from the surface will prevent the arc striking at all. Nothing will happen until enough filler wire has been extended to reduce the gap sufficiently for the arc to jump. However, the results will be uncontrollable, gas shielding will be ineffective and the arc very irratic.

Positioning the torch too close will often allow the arc to form, but not always. The most common consequence is a damaged contact tip, which may become distorted with heat or welded to the filler wire tip. The recommended height for the torch is 2-3mm above the surface.

WIRE AND GAS OPTIONS

Most modern DIY machines are supplied complete with a spool of filler wire. Normally this is a general purpose wire – copper-coated mild steel – measuring 0.6mm in diameter. Thicker 0.8mm is readily available for heavier duty applications.

For more specialised jobs different filler wire choices have to be made. As a general rule, the wire must be matched to the metal being welded but this can cause problems with the welding of aluminium and stainless steel because the match must be exact.

Unless you know the precise composition of the alloy being welded – there are many types of both aluminium and stainless steel – an accurate match will be impossible and quality results hard to achieve.

Unless the match is precise ultimate weld strength will suffer because the filler wire will not be fully compatible with the subject metal and complete fusion will not occur.

For general purpose welding on steel there are various gas options available. Argon, carbon dioxide and mixtures of the two are the common choices. Smaller machines are supplied with disposable canisters of gas and, although these are not particularly economical, replacements are readily available from most motoring superstores.

It makes better financial sense to rent a larger cylinder from a specialist supplier such as BOC. There are now depots nationwide and the whole procedure has been simplified in recent years.

Once the arc has formed it is vital to start moving the torch along the joint immediately. Dallying in one position will blow a hole and very probably ruin the job. Speed of torch movement is yet another essential factor.

It is one of the primary factors governing the overall quality of the weld. Essentially, moving too fast will not give the weld sufficient time to form, while moving too slowly will simply blow the metal away.

Strength in depth

The key to weld strength is adequate penetration. A good weld will extend right down through the thickness of the subject metal and protrude slightly from the bottom face. If this does not happen then complete fusion will not

have occurred and the weld will be weak. Speeding the torch along the joint will result in poor penetration and a sub-standard joint.

There is certainly a lot to remember when you first start, and developing the co-ordination of movement required will take time. The problems are compounded by having to view the whole process through a necessarily dark green filter. Built in to a face or head shield, these heavily tinted lenses are essential for preventing damage to the eyes and skin.

The electric arc radiates intense ultra-violet light which will burn unprotected skin in seconds and damage unshielded eyes equally quickly. Watching through such a dark filter makes assessing what's going on doubly difficult...

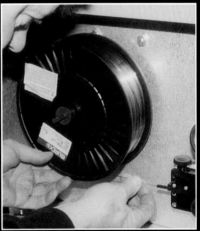

1. Most MIGs are supplied with a spool of filler wire these days. It is important to make sure that this is tensioned properly so follow the manufacturer's instructions. Do it up too tight and you will over-load the wire feed mechanism. Leave it too loose and the slack created will cause problems.

2. Threading the filler wire between the tensioning rollers should be simple. Some rollers are reversible – the cut grooves being of different widths so that varying diameters of wire can be used – so make sure the groove suits the wire you are threading. Tighten down the rollers as recommended in the instructions.

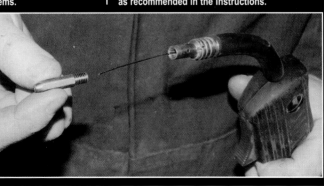

3. Drive the wire up the cable to the torch. It is advisable to remove the contact tip during this operation. If the end of the wire is not cleanly cut it can snag and become buckled.

4. Set the wire speed and voltage controls to 'average' positions – the instruction booklet for your machine should provide guidance but settings really are a matter of trial and error.

5. Adjusting the gas flow rate is important. This is the type of regulator found on large, 'professional' cylinders. Entry-level MIGs come with disposable canisters, often fitted simply with the ball bearing-type flow meter seen on the right.

It is very hard to describe to a novice exactly what to look for when using a MIG torch. Just being able to follow the line of the joint with the torch is one thing, let alone cooly assess its progress as you procede.

You see, MIG welding is a very interactive process. It requires constant attention, continual assessment and frequent but minute adjustments in technique. Once you get used to studying the arc you will learn to pick out the 'weld pool' into which it falls.

This tiny pool of molten metal must span the width of the joint at all times, as evenly as possible. The objective is to coax it along the joint at just the right speed to ensure complete penetration. Dawdling will allow too much of the metal to become molten, causing it to fall away producing a gaping hole.

Quite simply there is no substitute for practice, and plenty of it, when starting out with a MIG. Consistency of results is the name of the game and you will only achieve this with perseverence. Spend lots of time making practice runs on scrap metal. Early on it's just not worth bothering about trying to join pieces together, simply concentrate on producing straight, even runs without burning holes.

Developing the ability to lay down a consistently good 'bead' of weld across a piece of metal is an achievement in it-

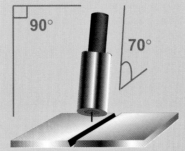

self. Until you reach this stage it really is not worth attempting any joints.

To begin with you will find it hard to keep the torch moving in a straight line, difficult to maintain the arc and almost impossible to see what's going on. However, persistence will bring its reward – most people develop reasonable ability given time – but your progress cannot be rushed.

Control settings are a matter of trial and error until your experience and judgement levels develop. Your machine will have adjustments for wire feed speed and voltage but, because every unit is different, it's impossible to generalise. Dial in some average set-

tings and just have a go.

The best way to deveolop an understanding of the subtle interplay between wire speed, voltage setting and torch movement is to learn through experience. No book or magazine can impart this knowledge. Doing it yourself or watching an expert are the only routes to eventual success.

You can make life easier for yourself by adopting a comfortable stance. Supporting and guiding the torch should be your central objective so it helps if your body is relaxed and comfortable.

A final word of advice. Do not be tempted to 'have a go' at any serious car-related repairs before you are utterly convinced about your own ability. Using a MIG for real will often involve welding vertically, or even overhead – access will be dictated by the type of repair and the vehicle involved. This will be far removed from your convenient and well-practiced test runs, and will demand new levels of skill and control.

Also, when working 'for real' it will often not be possible to check the reverse side of the weld for complete penetration. You must be totally confident about the thoroughness of your technique – lives may well be depending on it.

NEXT MONTH
Popular MIGs on test.

6. The return clamp must be securely attached to a clean, paint-free part of the workpiece. A poor electrical contact here will prevent the arc from being formed.

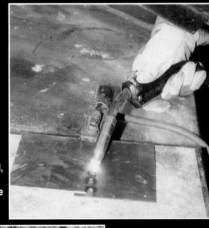

7. A helpful technique, when getting started, is to rest the nozzle of the torch directly on the workpiece. This will ensure that it remains steady as it moves and, if it's angled correctly, the required gap for the arc to form will be created.

8. Hand-held face shields are all very well but the full-face, hinged variety makes life easier for the beginner – it keeps both hands free for supporting the torch.

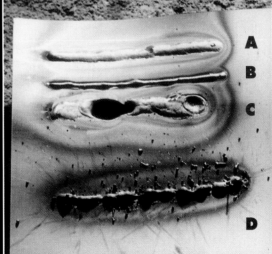

9. How your results can differ. **A** – A neat and regular weld bead – just how it should be. **B** – A thin and stringy bead lacking penetration. Here the torch is being moved too fast and/or the voltage is set too low. **C** – Blown holes – typical of slow torch movement or the voltage being too high. **D** – An untidy weld surrounded by 'spatter'. This happens if the wire feed is set too fast and/or the voltage is too high.

METAL MANAGEMENT

MIG WELDERS TEST

We put a group of MIGs through their paces. Chris Graham reports on our findings

Buying a MIG is easier said than done these days. Sure, they are all but falling off the shelves in most good DIY and motorist superstores, but the trouble is that there is almost too much choice.

Prices vary enormously across the market because the discount war is raging – shopping around really is a must in this business. Unfortunately, most buyers set too much store on cost. While it is certainly important, buying the cheapest brand you can find should never be your primary aim.

Choosing a MIG is all about matching the machine to your own requirements. You must consider how often it will be used, and for what type of work. Overall durability might be a significant factor too, particularly at the semi-professional and professional end of the scale.

Reliability and longevity will both be vital aspects if you are 'in the trade'. Having a machine which will work predictably and consistently could make the difference between being paid for a job or not. If things do go wrong then technical support and efficient spares supply from the manufacturer will be important to you as well.

The group of machines we assembled for testing fall into two distinct groups, with one exception. All come from popular suppliers who are major players in the market. Their machines are widely available through nationwide distributor networks and independent sources, so all are easy to get hold of.

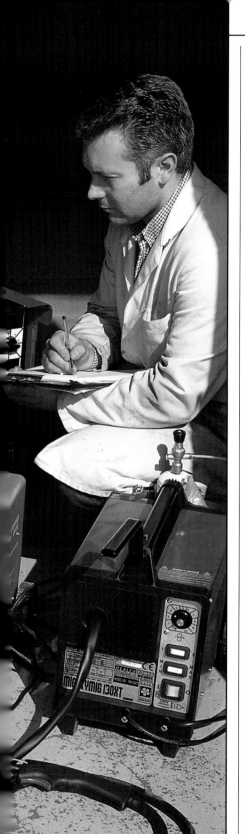

We decided to split the test between a group of larger machines aimed at the serious DIY user/professional operator, and a selection from lower down the scale, priced more specifically for the first time buyer.

We purposely avoided the absolute entry-level machines – the 100A mini MIGs and 'no gas' machines. We've looked at these basic babies before and nothing much has changed since then. Additionally, by spending just a little bit more cash and moving up to a 130A machine, you get a much better deal. The unit is likely to boast a cooling fan so its duty cycle will be greatly enhanced – basically it'll work for longer without getting too hot and cutting out.

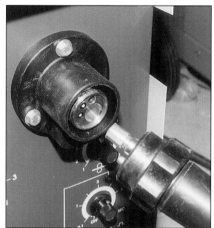

A Euro-type torch connector like this makes a lot of sense for the professional user. Torches can be swapped with ease between machines.

In addition, the step-up to these slightly larger machines generally brings with it the benefits of better quality components. Items such as the transformer and wire feed mechanism will normally be superior to their equivalents on the base models and these advantages will boost the machine's controllability in use.

The arc will be that little bit more stable, the wire feed will be more consistent and the whole thing should generally be easier to get on with – important factors if you are a beginner.

Testing times

Assessing the performance of a MIG welder is a very personal thing. Much depends upon the ability of the tester and his skill in drawing the best out of the machine. From an objective point of view, however, this is not what we are after here.

Our aim was to establish how well these machines worked 'straight out of the box'. How easy they were to set up, how clear and informative the instructions were and how accurately any control setting suggestions provided related to real life.

This last aspect is, after all, the crux of the matter as far as the novice is concerned. If you are new to the technique then the manufacturer's setting suggestions for wire speed and voltage levels are all you will have to work with. If they are hopeless then you are left grappling with trial and error – not the most productive or encouraging way to get started.

Because we had split the machines into two groups we thought it appropriate to divide the testing as well. For the expert view we tapped the experienced impressions of Bill How, a lecturer in Vehicle Body Repair in the School of Auto Engineering at the Colchester Institute.

As a more practical alternative, we also sought the views of two of the Institute's students, Michael Carter and Chris Wood. Both have basic welding ability but neither is expert at the technique.

We encouraged these two to set up the MIGs, following the instructions and control guidelines to the letter, exactly as a new owner would do. Then they were set the task of making three test welds – two butt and a T-joint – with each machine.

The test impressions which follow represent their honest and unbiased views as first-time users, plus overall comments from Bill. Prices were kept secret during testing.

Turn over for test results

The testers – from left to right: Michael Carter, Bill How and Chris Woods. A mixture of professional and relatively inexperienced MIG users insured a comprehensive assessment.

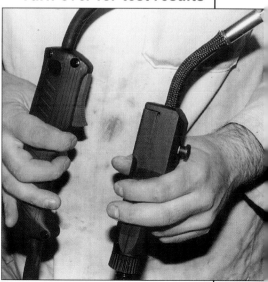

The torch on the left features a full size trigger which the testers preferred to the push-button type on the right. They found it easier to use.

RESTORATION REPRINT BOOKS
from Kelsey Publishing

All Kelsey reprint books are compiled from serialised features from the magazines shown on the book covers. They are produced from the original film and printed on the finest paper. This ensures the best possible quality.

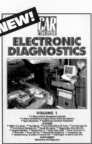

NEW!

Electronic Diagnostics Volume 1

A collation of the *Car Mechanics* Engine Management Systems series.

£14.95 + £2 p&p (UK)

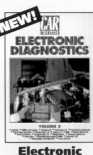

NEW!

Electronic Diagnostics Volume 2

More engine management systems covered for the serious DIY enthusiast and the trade.

£14.95 + £2 p&p (UK)

Mini Cooper Restoration

Restoration, including chassis repair, sills, replacing the roof and boot floor, spraying, engine rebuild, suspension, trim.

£10.95 + £2 p&p (UK)

MGB GT Restoration

The only full colour step-by-step MG B restoration published. Includes buying guide, restoration right through to road test. 112 pages.

£15.95 + £2 p&p (UK)

Ford Escort Mechanics

Guide to Escort mechanics plus buying guide, uprating, alternator and carburettor rebuilds. 100 pages mainly in colour.

£14.95 + £2 p&p (UK)

Ford Capri Restoration

Restoration of a 2.8i, 1.6 and bodywork on a Mk1. Plus Pinto engine, V6 Essex engine & carburettor rebuilds.

£14.95 + £2 p&p (UK)

Mk2 Jaguar

Step-by-step DIY restoration guide. Over 100 pages, mostly in colour.

£14.95 + £2 p&p (UK)

Jaguar XK 120 Restoration

The most comprehensive step-by-step restoration of an XK 120 ever undertaken covering chassis, body and engine etc. 128 pages

£16.95 + £2 p&p (UK)

Jaguar Six-Cyl. Engine Overhaul

In depth engine rebuild, including IRS and SU carburettor overhaul. 94 pages (many in colour).

£12.95 + £2 p&p (UK)

Jaguar XJ6 Restoration

The best step-by-step DIY restoration of this model ever undertaken. 128 pages and over 450 illustrations.

£14.95 + £2 p&p (UK)

Panel Beating & Paint

The best work on the subject of panel beating ever produced. Over 90 pages many in full colour.

£12.95 + £2 p&p (UK)

Classic Auto Electrics

Includes component overhauls, trouble shooting and rewiring. Over 100 pages.

£9.95 + £2 p&p (UK)

Welding & Welders

Includes all the DIY welding methods available and how to use them, with emphasis on MIG welding. 70 pages.

£8.95 + £2 p&p (UK)

Classic Trim

Step-by-step DIY restoration guide for classic car trim. Over 70 pages, many in colour.

£10.95 + £2 p&p (UK)

2CV Restoration

Restoration of a 2CV including new replacement chassis, bodywork repairs, checking and servicing of mechanicals. Fitting Lumenition & refurbishing

£8.95 + £2 p&p (UK)

Minor Traveller Restoration

Step-by-step DIY restoration guide. 96 pages with 400 illustartions, many in colour.

£12.95 + £2 p&p (UK)

Triumph TR6

A step-by-step DIY restoration guide. 100 pages (most in colour) and 350 illustrations.

£14.95 + £2 p&p (UK)

Triumph Spitfire Restoration

Best ever step-by-step DIY Spitfire restoration. 100 pages.

£14.95 + £2 p&p (UK)

Triumph Herald

Step-by-step DIY restoration guide. Over 100 pages (including colour).

£14.95 + £2 p&p (UK)

Triumph Stag

A step-by-step DIY restoration guide. Over 100 pages, many in colour.

£14.95 + £2 p&p (UK)

MGB

In two parts - MGB uprating and also MGB bodyshell restoration. Over 100 pages, inc. colour.

£10.95 + £2 p&p (UK)

Scimitar

Includes mechanical overhauls, glass fibre repair and painting, buying guide etc. 70 pages.

£8.95 + £2 p&p (UK)

Post coupon to: Books Department, Kelsey Publishing Ltd., PO Box 13, Westerham, Kent TN16 3WT. Tel: 01959 541444 Fax: 01959 541400

Please send me: (prices shown here include UK postage)
- ❏ Electronic Diagnostics Volume 1 (Car Mechanics) @ £16.95
- ❏ Electronic Diagnostics Volume 2 (Car Mechanics) @ £16.95
- ❏ Mini Cooper Restoration (Practical Classics) @ £12.95
- ❏ MGB GT Restoration (Practical Classics) @ £17.95
- ❏ Ford Escort Mechanics (Car Mechanics) @ £16.95
- ❏ Ford Capri Restoration (Practical Class./Car Mech.) @ £16.95
- ❏ Mk2 Jaguar Restoration (Practical Classics) @ £16.95
- ❏ Jaguar XK 120 Restoration (Jaguar Enthusiast) @ £18.95
- ❏ Jaguar Six Cylinder Engine Overhaul (Jaguar World) @ £14.95
- ❏ Jaguar XJ6 Restoration (Jaguar Enthusiast) @ £16.95
- ❏ Panel Beating & Paint Refinishing (Car Mechanics) @ £14.95
- ❏ Classic Auto Electrics (Practical Classics) @ £11.95
- ❏ Welding Techniques & Welders (Practical Classics) @ £10.95
- ❏ Classic Trim (Practical Classics) @ £12.95
- ❏ 2CV Restoration (Car Mechanics) @ £10.95
- ❏ Minor Traveller Restoration (Practical Classics) @ £14.95
- ❏ Triumph TR6 Restoration (Practical Classics) @ £16.95
- ❏ Triumph Spitfire Restoration (Practical Classics) @ £16.95
- ❏ Triumph Herald/Vitesse Restoration (Practical C) @ £16.95
- ❏ Triumph Stag Restoration (Practical Classics) @ £16.95
- ❏ MGB Uprating & Bodyshell Rebuild (Practical C) @ £12.95
- ❏ Scimitar Restoration (Practical Classics) @ £ 10.95

FOR OVERSEAS ORDERS ADD EXTRA £2 PER BOOK TO THESE PRICES FOR SURFACE MAIL, EXTRA £4 FOR AIRMAIL.

I enclose my cheque, made payable to **KELSEY PUBLISHING**, for £ ....

(or) please debit my ❏ EUROCARD MasterCard ❏ VISA ❏ SWITCH ❏ AMERICAN EXPRESS

No: ....

Expiry date: .... Switch Issue No: .... Signature: ....

Name: ....
BLOCK CAPITALS PLEASE

Address: ....

....

POSTCODE ....

KB

Clarke Turboweld 130TE

BEST BUY!

First impressions were very encouraging with this machine, which appeared to be well built and generally sturdy. The instructions were excellent, written in plain English, and included some useful exploded views of the welder and its component parts – very helpful for maintenance and servicing.

Although the machine was supplied pre-built we were disappointed to find no plug was fitted and that the lead-in lengths of filler wire showed signs of rusting. Nevertheless, the control switches felt solid and durable, despite looking identical to most of the others.

In use, the testers were very impressed with the 130TE. They found the manufacturer's guidance on control settings to be extremely accurate – it worked first time and produced good quality welds in each of the three tests. You cannot ask for more than that.

The conclusion was that this machine constitutes an excellent first-time buy, with everything necessary supplied in the kit.

Clarke 185T Turbo

This higher spec, more powerful machine from Clarke benefited from equally clear and informative instructions. The recommended settings were found to be spot-on.

Setting up as instructed enabled the machine to produce first class welds in each instance – it was the only MIG in the test to gain full marks for weld quality.

Once again, however, no plug was supplied, which proved a minor irritation, especially during a group test. One other missing component was a gas regulator.

The final comment from both students who used this machine was: "I want one!". The quality of its construction was

impressive, although it was a shame that no Euro torch coupling was included.

Esab LKA150

This welder was the exception to the classification rule, being rated at 150-amps. Esab do not produce anything 'smaller' than the LKA150 so this, effectively, is their entry-level offering.

Unfortunately, Esab were unable to provide us with a new example for the test. The machine featured here belongs to the college but we felt it warranted inclusion nonetheless.

A consequence of its secondhand status was that we had no instructions to refer to or judge but, fortunately, the machine is supplied ready assembled.

The LKA150 features professional-type dial controls which sets it apart from all the other 'starter' MIGs included here – the rest all feature rocker-type switches. The machine also features a full-sized torch.

On the downside, concerns were expressed about the plastic front panel and the protruding dial controls which could both suffer from impact damage.

The testers found the dials easy to work with and simpler to set-up than the combination of rockers favoured by the others. The machine worked well and produced very good welds in all three tests.

The conclusion was that this Esab unit represents a professional quality welder in a compact case.

Sealey Mightymig 130XT

The testers were disappointed with the instructions supplied with this machine. They found them unclear and inadequate. There was very little detail about assembly, which was particularly unfortunate because this MIG was supplied partially dismantled.

It took over an hour to ready the machine for use – even the face shield had

to be put together. When compared to the 'ready for action' state of some of the others, this was unacceptable.

The unit was found to have no light built into the on/off switch and the wire speed control proved to be very erratic. Even slight movements of the dial resulted in disproportionately large speed changes.

The recommended settings bore little relation to those actually needed, so achieving good quality welds was tricky initially. The situation was not helped by the 'wandering' wire feed and the fact that, in places, the filler wire supplied was actually rusty.

On the positive side the welder was supplied with a comprehensive starter kit and a good selection of useful spares.

Sealey Supermig 185

Unfortunately, this larger offering from Sealey fared little better than its 130-amp cousin. Owners are supplied with identical instructions so all the comments already mentioned hold true here too.

Build quality was reasonably good and the testers were impressed with the inclusion of a Euro-torch plug and socket combination. Spot and tack weld facilities are also included on this machine.

Once the correct settings were established, weld performance was reasonably good.

The testers were disappointed by the small reel of filler wire supplied (0.2kg) with this machine – virtually exhausted during testing due to poor winding and a rusty section.

The final verdict was that the Supermig 185 felt like little more than an enlarged-case version of the Mightymig.

SIP MigmateTurbo 130

Once again the testers reported disappointment with the instructional literature supplied with this machine. They

	Typical price	Weight	Instructions	Ease of Weld use	Quality	Points tot. (max 30)
Clarke 130 TE	£189	28.5kg	9	8	8	25
Clarke 185T Turbo	£429	47kg	9	8	10	27
Esab LKA150	£468	34kg	–	8	8	16/20
Sealey Mightymig 130XT	£304	23kg	3	5	6	14
Sealey Supermig 185	£551	43.5kg	3	6	7	16
Sureweld Monomig 121	£246	24kg	8	7	7	22
Sureweld Monomig 181	£466	50kg	9	8	7	24
SIP Migmate Turbo 130	£219	28kg	3	5	8	16
SIP Autoplus Turbo 196	£468	50kg	2	6	8	16

(Prices include VAT)

Sureweld Monomig 181

Although the instruction booklet supplied with this machine appeared similar to the one packaged with the Monomig 121, the guide setting information was far more accurate and received much praise from the testers. They were able to produce good quality welds immediately using the information provided.

Overall construction was found to be of a high quality and in use the 181 passed the weld tests with flying colours, producing strong and presentable joints in each of the three tests. Despite not featuring a Euro-style connection, the big Sureweld's torch, with its more conventional elongated trigger, was well received, together with the machine's quality cable.

Effective tack and spot weld facilities completed the picture for this desirable and well-made welder.

Our recommendations

Reaching absolute conclusions about which machine to buy is always tricky – there are so many variables and, after all, the whole testing procedure is very subjective.

Nevertheless, a winner there must be. Bill How's verdict, viewing the machines as overall packages was that, given the choice, he would opt for the **Clarke 130TE** and the **SIP Autoplus Turbo 196.**

This Clarke unit finished second in our points rating (see table) but this is only half the story. The machine is well made, very easy to set up, appears durable and customers are supplied with everything for an immediate start. Those new to MIG will benefit particularly from the quality instructions.

Of the bigger machines, Bill chose the SIP Autoplus as his favourite, not because it scored the most points – it didn't – but because it combined high quality construction with good performance and the significant professional asset of a Euro-style torch connection. An excellent choice for the workshop.

NEXT MONTH
GAS WELDING

---

considered it extremely basic with no reference to guide settings etc at all. Consequently setting-up took longer than it should and was reduced to a matter of trial and error – no help to the beginner.

However, once up and running this machine did impress with the quality of the welds it produced. In each test case they were strong, even and very presentable. The testers liked its durable all-steel construction, the integral front handle – sturdier than the bar extension offerings from most of the others – and the quality torch.

One concern centred on the wire feed mechanism. Made predominantly of plastic – most are these days – the unit in this machine had a decidedly flimsy feel about it and had to be tightened up to get it to drive effectively. There was obvious play in the shafts and the whole assembly had the feel of one that would deteriorate with age.

SIP Autoplus Turbo 196

The larger SIP machine proved to be a much stronger performer in all respects, apart from its instructions. These were found to be even more basic than those for the Migmate – again, no help with control settings.

Now, while there is an argument which suggests that instructions for a professional-type machine are perhaps less essential than at the DIY end of the market, there really is no excuse for such brief literature – after all, every owner finds practical, user-friendly information of some value.

A plug-in Euro-type torch was included with this machine, (which is a significant benefit) as well as an all-steel construction. It was impressively put together, and the design featured four wheels (castors at the front) making it easy to manoeuvre.

Wire feed was a significant improvement over the Migmate, with a more sturdy steel construction. The machine also featured a timer, which could be used for spot and tack-weld work and this worked reasonably well.

Sureweld Monomig 121

The testers commented on the good and clear instructional literature provided with this machine. Useful assembly information was included but, as the 121 came ready-built, this was not required.

Set-up was achieved relatively quickly, despite the lack of a plug. Overall construction levels were good and the unit featured an impressively solid front handle, but a black mark was awarded for rusty filler wire.

In use, the biggest criticism was of the push-button torch control. The testers did not like this system, preferring the more common and larger trigger arrangement used by all the others here. They claimed that there was a tendency for the gloved finger to slip off the small button, which reduced torch control levels and ease of operation.

However, the 121 produced some neat, strong welds and proved a usable machine once the trigger button had been mastered.

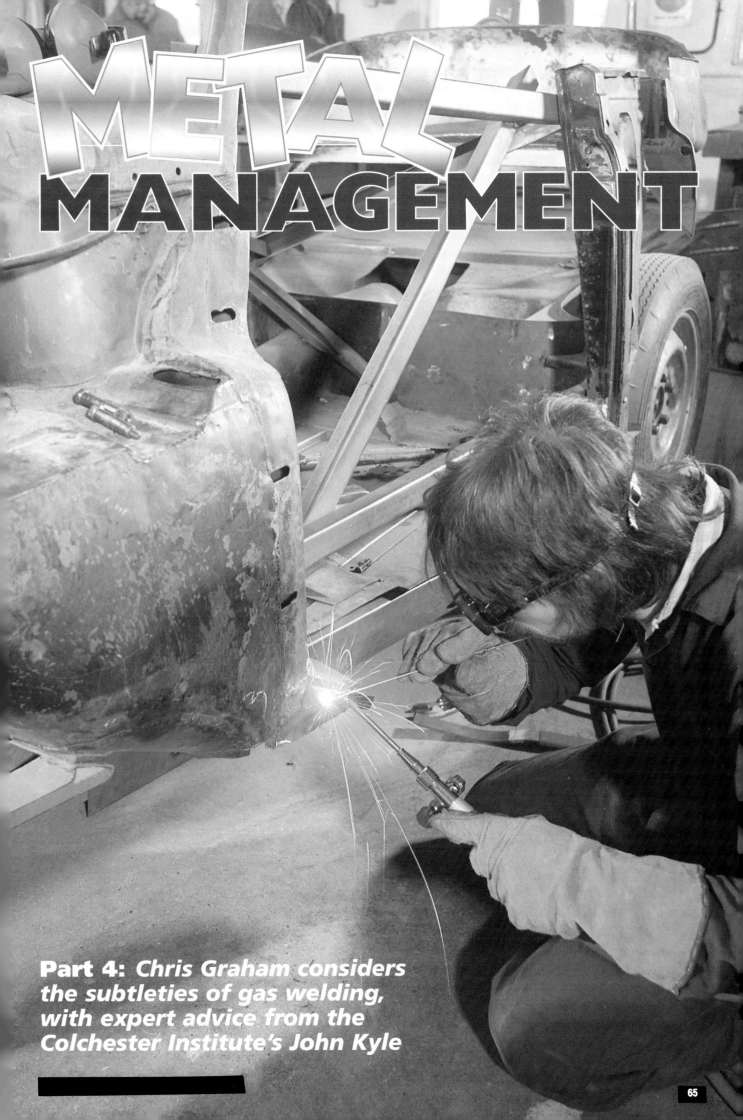

METAL MANAGEMENT

Part 4: Chris Graham considers the subtleties of gas welding, with expert advice from the Colchester Institute's John Kyle

The popularity of gas welding has waned over the past 15 years, with much emphasis now being placed on the MIG/MAG process. Nevertheless, you'd be quite wrong to reject gas out of hand because it boasts some very significant advantages over the newer techniques.

Foremost among these is its impressive versatility. A gas set, quite apart from being used to create top-quality welds on virtually every commonly-found metal, can also be used as a heat source for brazing and soldering; for warming up and freeing seized components; as an aid to shaping metal; for inducing the annealing process essential for softening work-hardened steel and for cutting.

Then there is the 'go anywhere' nature of the equipment. Gas users are not tied to the nearest mains electricity socket and the technique can be used outside as effectively as it can in. Finally, and perhaps most significantly of

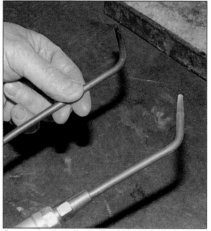

Correct nozzle selection is vital, particularly when welding thin sheet metal. Remember that it is the size of the hole in the nozzle which effectively controls the 'power' of the flame – the greater the diameter, the hotter the flame.

all, there is the sheer excellence of the results to be considered. In the right hands a gas torch can produce the neatest, strongest and most controllable of welds. 'Traditionalists' still swear by the technique.

On the downside there is the small matter of difficulty. Regarded by many as the most technically demanding technique, using gas equipment properly is certainly an acquired art.

WHAT'S INVOLVED?

Gas welding is made possible by the combustion of a mixture of two gases – oxygen and acetylene – hence the term oxy-acetylene. It is the acetylene which is the flammable one of the pair, the oxygen merely aids combustion when both are mixed. The secret of this combination is that it burns at an extremely high temperature. Steel melts at about 1,200°C but the gas flame reaches temperatures of over 3,000°C. There's a lot of power involved – we're talking hot stuff!

The two gases are supplied to the torch or blowpipe from separate, colour-coded, high pressure steel cylinders. Those containing oxygen,

always coloured black, have their contents compressed to 3,332psi (230 bar) but because acetylene is a more unstable compound it is stored at a significantly lower pressure.

Due to its general sensitivity the acetylene has first to be dissolved into acetone and the mixture then pumped into a steel cylinder – always colour-coded maroon – containing a porous substance such as kapok. These cylinders are never charged to more than 224psi (15.5 bar).

Apart from the different colours, oxygen and acetylene cylinders are also distinguished by right and left-hand threaded valve sockets respectively. This safety-related precaution also applies to all hose and torch threads relating to the two gases.

Regulator valves are employed to control the gas supply leaving each cylinder. These are two-stage units which perform a couple of important functions. They exert direct control over gas pressure which is a vital factor

This screw-on device is an automatic flashback arrestor. It represents an essential safety component and one should be fitted to both oxygen and acetylene cylinder outlets. In the event of excessive pressure build up, of if the hose is burning internally, the arrestor acts to seal off the gas supply.

The gas regulator must be set accurately to control pressure at the nozzle. The dial on the right shows cylinder pressure (contents) while the one on the left denotes the set working pressure – this is the one which responds to adjustments made with the central control.

MANAGEMENT

in the welding process.

It must be stepped down from cylinder pressure to a working pressure at the torch of, for example, just 2psi when welding car body-thickness metal – a surprisingly low level. In addition it's the regulator's job to ensure that flow rates remain the same, irrespective of the amount of gas left in the cylinder.

The gas is piped separately to the torch, sometimes called a blowpipe, where it is mixed and then channelled out through the nozzle (or tip) to be ignited. Individual, colour-coded valves mounted on the torch body control the flow of both gases.

These provide the only adjustment potential for the user and their accurate setting is central to the success of the process. The proportions in which the two gases are burnt has a significant effect on the type of flame produced. Get it wrong by failing to recognise the clearly visible signs and the weld quality will suffer.

THE HEAT IS ON

There is a fixed procedure for lighting the torch (see box) and this is one which must always be followed. Once alight, the flame must be 'tuned' to match the intended use. For most work – with steel, stainless steel, aluminium, cast iron, copper etc – a 'neutral' flame should be your setting objective.

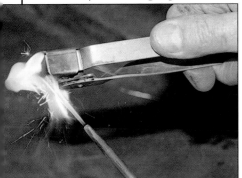

To light a gas torch switch on the acetylene ONLY and always use a spark igniter like this.

This is achieved when equal quantities of oxygen and acetylene are being burnt. Variations in the flow rates of one or other of the gases are employed for specific effects. An excess of acetylene creates what's called a 'carburizing' flame. This is characterised by a white feather which surrounds the blue cone at the centre of the flame. A mixture of this sort produces an excess of unburnt carbon, and adds this to the weld, making it harder but also more brittle.

For normal use a carburizing flame is not a good idea, for obvious reasons. However, for surface hardening, when intentionally laying down extra carbon will case-harden a metal surface, it is ideal.

Introducing more oxygen to the equation produces an 'oxidising' flame. This is denoted by a smaller flame overall, an increase in 'flame hiss' and a reduced and more pointed cone at the centre. Using this type of flame to conventionally weld steel will produce excessive sparking, a very poor quality joint and will probably blow holes into the bargain. The finished weld will be weak and plenty of slag will be visible on the surface.

The established use for an oxidising flame is in the welding of brass and bronzes, where the effects of the extra oxidation are a necessity. When used on brass it helps prevent the zinc coating from being burnt off.

There is one other variable to be considered and this is the size of the nozzle. The diameter of the hole in the end must be varied according to the thickness of metal being welded. These are classified in a number of ways but most commonly in the UK this information is denoted by a simple figure stamped on the side.

Although the numbers used do not appear to relate specifically to the dimension involved, the general rule is 'the larger the number, the bigger the outlet hole'. Note that nozzles are not numbered consecutively (see table) and that for sizes above No7, working pressure has to be increased.

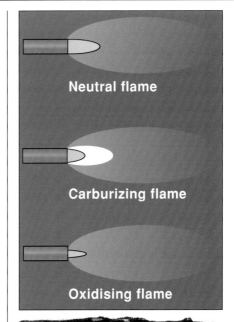

Neutral flame

Carburizing flame

Oxidising flame

Lighting up

1. **Always switch on acetylene first**
2. **Ignite gas with approved spark lighter and nozzle facing away**
3. **Slowly increase acetylene flow until smoking stops**
4. **Gradually introduce oxygen**
5. **Increase flow until blue cone becomes clearly defined at base of flame**

Note: *Never light torch with a gas-powered cigarette lighter or match. Both of these present potential safety hazards in the workshop and neither should be involved in the welding process on safety grounds.*

GETTING STARTED

Gas welding is a precise technique which requires high levels of manual dexterity and hand-eye co-ordination. It is a skill which must be practised and probably, if we are being brutally honest, it's not a technique which everyone can master.

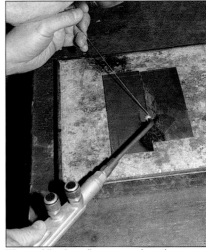

When welding keep fingers away from the gas controls on the torch. A common mistake that beginners make is to nudge these unintentionally which upsets the balance of the flame to adversely affect weld quality.

Once alight, increase the flow of acetylene – red control – until the flame stops smoking, then use the blue control to gradually introduce the oxygen. Continue increasing its flow rate until a clearly defined blue cone is formed.

Gloves are optional when gas welding. Torch-to-panel distance is essential – the hottest part of the flame must be played continuously on the joint.

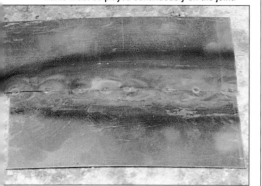

When working with thin sheet it makes sense to tack the joint before welding. Heat spread with gas equipment is significant so distortion is always a problem. Tacking every centimetre or so will hold the joint in alignment as welding progresses. As a general rule the gap between pieces being joined should equal diameter of filler rod.

Unlike MIG welding, gas is very often a two-handed process. There are cases when, due to a very close-fitting joint, just the flame can be used to fuse the joint together. But in most instances a filler rod must be introduced as the weld progresses to ensure good levels of strength.

Filler rods must match the metal being welded. With steel subjects this is not a problem and standard, copper-coated wire will be fine. But with other metals filler rod choice can be an involved business. The effective welding of aluminium, for example, requires an accurate match.

This is easy enough if you know what you are dealing with – perhaps you may be able to use strips cut from the parent metal as filler rods – but with older, 'unknown' alloys the situation can be very difficult. Aged alu-

Whenever you stop mid-way through a weld run a crater like this will be produced. When re-starting always re-weld over this to ensure full strength. Whenever possible check the rear of the weld for signs of complete penetration. This is your guarantee of ultimate weld strength.

minium will almost certainly suffer from some degree of oxidation which further adds to the problems.

Aluminium is a difficult material to gas weld at the best of times and, indeed, beginners can experience technical problems even with straightforward steel. As with all forms of welding, getting the best from a gas torch is all about understanding the variables and being able to read the signs.

For a start, nozzle-to-surface distance is vital. The trick is always to use the hottest part of the flame so that the subject metal is heated as rapidly as possible. This is between two and five millimetres in front of the tip of the blue centre cone, where temperatures soar to 3,200°C.

Getting this positioning wrong is bad news. Holding the torch too far away simply spreads the heat over a wider area and increases the risk of distortion, while placing it too close will deflect the cone to cause undesirables such as hole blowing, back-firing and a generally unstable flame.

In addition to holding the torch at exactly the right distance from the subject, it must also be angled correctly and moved along the joint at a suitable speed. Torch angle varies with the direction of travel (see diagram) and speed of movement is essentially determined by metal thickness. Generally, if you progress too slowly then you'll blow holes and if you speed along then penetration and so weld strength will be inadequate.

Earlier we touched on the importance of setting the right gas working pressure and this cannot be over-emphasised. When working on thin metal, such as body panels, deviations

from the recommended 2psi at the nozzle can be disastrous.

Settings higher than this will lead to overheating of the joint and the creation of every welder's arch enemy, holes. This is a very common problem. Conversely, pressure set below 2psi is likely to produce an inconsistent flame and back-firing – the flame will momentarily be extinguished and then re-light itself, accompanied by a shower of sparks. This makes consistent welding impossible.

As far as technique is concerned there are two basic approaches and the choice between these is governed by the thickness of the metal being welded. Referring to the diagram you will note that leftward welding involves the torch being moved from right to left along the joint.

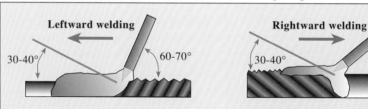

Leftward welding 30-40° 60-70°

Rightward welding 30-40° 40-50°

This progression must be accompanied by slight side-to-side or circular movement of the torch so that the joint is straddled evenly. The angle of the torch required for leftward welding ensures that the flame pre-heats the joint effectively. This method is recommended for metal up to 5mm thick.

For thicker subjects the approach is best switched to rightward welding. The torch is maintained at a shallower angle, and tilted in the direction of travel – the filler rod follows on behind.

Only after plenty of experimentation will you begin to appreciate how these factors all relate to each other. Practice is the only sure way to develop your talent for gas welding, a process which many in the trade consider the most difficult of the welding disciplines.

NEXT MONTH
TIG welding

NOZZLE GUIDE

Metal thickness	Nozzle size	Oxy/acet pressure
0.9mm	No.1	2psi
1.2mm	No.2	2psi
2mm	No.3	2psi
2.6mm	No.5	2psi
3.2mm	No.7	2psi
4mm	No.10	3psi
5mm	No.13	4psi

METAL
MANAGEMENT

Part 5:
Chris Graham explores the intricacies of TIG welding and discovers why it's not as popular as MIG

The fact that TIG welding has never caught on to the same degree as MIG is not a surprising one. Despite its all-round excellence – referred to by many as the Rolls-Royce of techniques – the potential problems outweigh the benefits in all but the most specialised of situations.

Those who have been waiting for TIG hardware prices to tumble are still waiting. The advent of 'inverter' technology brought with it the promise of reduced costs but, so far, the benefits are yet to be felt.

The hard facts are that even entry-level equipment is likely to set you back upwards of £800, while stand-alone, capital equipment costs £2,000+. TIG is not a process for the enthusiast operating on a budget, which is a great shame, because the results achievable are, quite simply, superb.

To discover more about the process I consulted the Colchester Institute's Michael Gray, who is a senior lecturer and expert in all things welding.

TIG BASICS

The letters 'TIG' stand for tungsten inert gas and relate to the primary components of the process. An electric arc is formed between the tip of a tungsten electrode and the metal being welded, and the heat from this leads to fusion of the metal.

In most cases a separate source of filler wire is required and must be fed in by hand. Unlike MIG, there is no continuous wire feed through the torch which is why TIG is a two-handed process. In common with MIG, however, TIG does rely on a supply of inert gas to shield the weld from contamination as it forms.

Normally this is pure Argon, but mixtures are available too. The choice of gas is determined by the type of material being welded. Mixtures of gases are generally employed to improve the quality and appearance of the weld – argon plus helium or hydrogen, for example. In reality, you can successfully weld the majority of common metals with argon alone but by selecting the appropriate mixture, quality will be enhanced.

Adding small quantities of hydrogen

Good ventilation is vital when using a TIG unit. Ideally, professionally installed extraction equipment like this from Nederman should be employed. Don't position extraction too close to the job or you will affect the inert gas shield.

improves the heat input and, therefore, the fusion. Gray says there are perhaps nine possible combinations used, with most being selected for the welding of assorted steels and non-ferrous materials.

The tungsten electrode, usually with a pointed tip, is officially classified as 'non-consumable' but, in practice, it does get gradually eroded. The exception to the pointed tip rule is for the welding of aluminium, when it must be blunted. The reasons for this are technical and need not concern us here.

This electrode is mounted in the torch and surrounded by a ceramic nozzle. The degree to which the tip protrudes beyond this insulator is an important factor and must be set to suit the joint being welded.

The workpiece, of course, must be

ALL UNDER CONTROL

The controls typically found on a high specification TIG unit consist of: an AC/DC selection switch; a DC polarity switch; an amperage selector – ideally stepless; 'slope in' and 'slope out' controls to create a progressive increase and decrease of power at the start and finish of the weld, minimising the risk of blowing holes and other weld defects; a 'post gas flow' control which allows the shielding gas to remain on after the arc has been extinguished – gives added protection to the weld and the tungsten tip as they both cool at the end of the weld; a 'Square wave' control which is a relatively new device for use on AC settings. This enables the user to change the half-cycles so that materials with a thick oxide layer can more effectively be welded.

On top of all this, the best units may also feature a pulsing control which helps guard against excessive heat build up on long runs by varying the current form. Supply is split into two – a background current which keeps the arc going, plus a high current pulse which is triggered at preset intervals to suit the job. The overall effect is a colder weld with minimal distortion plus enhanced and very even penetration along its entire length.

earthed, and there is also a conventional return lead, so that the current will flow and allow the arc to form. The supply of shielding gas is piped to the torch and emitted from around the tungsten tip to ensure good coverage. Its feed, together with the current, is controlled by a single micro-switch on the torch, although foot-controlled alternatives are available.

As with MIG, it is essential to match

High specification TIGs have plenty of controlability – see box (above).

METAL MANAGEMENT

the filler wire to the metal type being welded, so that sound fusion is ensured.

One of the biggest advantages of the TIG process is its cleanliness. The arc heat is intense and localised because it is formed from the tungsten tip. With MIG the arc jumps between the tip of a consumable electrode which contains deoxidants. These are transferred to the weld and can affect its quality.

With TIG this is not a factor for concern but it must be realised that joint preparation is vitally important. Remember that the benefits of a pure and inert arc will be lost if the metal being welded is itself smothered with impurities. To overcome any impurities already in the metal the rods are specially treated. Also, it takes more than just a grinding disc to clean the joint – ideally solvents should be employed for consistent results.

TIG is perhaps the most versatile of all the welding methods. Metals which are traditionally perceived as being complicated to weld, such as cast iron, are well within the scope of the TIG process. In addition, whenever 'exotic' materials have to be welded for specialist applications, the expert will often opt for a TIG unit.

There are exceptions, of course, and titanium is one. TIG will cope but the process is complicated by the involved attachments which are required. Fortunately, you don't find too much titanium on the average Rover 416!

THE HARDWARE

As I've mentioned already, TIG units do not come cheap. This is probably the main reason why the technique is limited to the specialist operators – racing car constructors who are working with exotic metals etc. Nevertheless, the prospects for the technique within the more general automotive sector may be on the up. The increasing use of aluminium and stainless steels in road car designs must soon start to bring TIG more to the fore.

In the meantime, choice of equipment is determined by cost. Top-spec machines cost a fortune and small ones just cost a lot! Fortunately, according to Gray, the difference in weld quality achievable at the two ends of the price scale is not that great. The extra money simply buys you an enhanced range of control options.

The quality of a TIG weld is based on the effective coverage of the shielding gas, the sharpness of the electrode

point, the correct selection of amperage and the operator's skill. Essentially, the cost of the equipment being used is irrelevant – you can theoretically create a top-notch joint with the most basic set.

Most of the larger machines can be run on either AC or DC current and the choice between the two relates to the metal being joined. For aluminium AC is required because of the cyclic nature which acts to lift and replace the oxide layer from the metal so that a sound weld can be made.

The DC option is used for virtually everything else, with the tungsten electrode always being selected as the negative terminal. The actual current setting is selected in relation to the heat conductivity and the mass of the metal. For example, stainless steel has very poor thermal conductivity properties so a lower amperage is required. Moving to steel, aluminium or copper, with higher electrical and thermal conductivity, the current input has to be raised to compensate.

Data sheets are available but they should only ever be regarded as guid-

Entry-level machines are far more basic but are nevertheless still expensive in MIG terms. However, performance of all is excellent.

ance on settings. Experience counts for more and this only comes after plenty of practice.

One of the fundamentals to bear in mind is that TIG welding requires a delicate touch, not what Gray describes as the 'Blacksmith's' approach which you can get away with when using arc or MIG equipment.

Previous experience with gas welding is probably the most relevant when learning to use a TIG unit. The arc should be regarded as an electrical 'flame' and used in the same way. The difference is that the arc is far more concentrated and so melts the metal more efficiently with less heat dissipation.

Setting the gas flow correctly is a very important factor – refer to data and make sure chosen level is accurate.

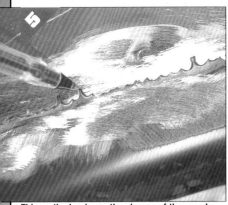

This method reduces the chance of the panel distorting but can result in pin-holing – a gap in the weld which shows when it's ground back. Ian intends to skim the repair with filler which is porous and could trap moisture, inviting rust to form. So, it's vital, on a wheel arch, to weld the gaps, preventing water getting in.

SPOT WELDING THE INNER PANELS

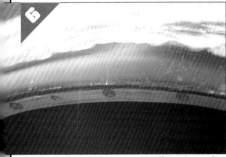

Montegos almost always rust on the outer and inner wheelarch, necessitating replacement of both panels. The inner arch is fitted, in a similar way to the outer, but the two panels' lips are joined by spot welding.

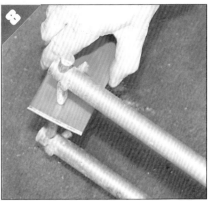

Before touching the car, take some scrap of the same gauge material and practise. Like any form of welding, the process takes experimentation to obtain best results. The electrode carrying arms are set so that, when clamped together, they are parallel.

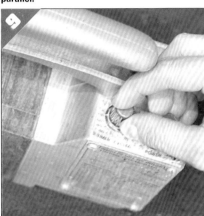

Ian explained the spot welder isn't difficult to use. But if you've never been shown, it's easy to get it wrong; the common mistake is too much power. Ian reported that they used to make a dozen spot welds and leave the machine to cool down because the electrodes glowed red hot. An old spot welding hand put SprayTech on the right track by explaining that for best results they should turn the current right down, using the timer function more. Then, welds are more controlled, resulting in longer welding time, without overheating the machine.

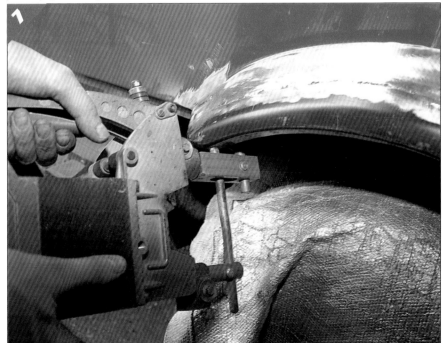

SprayTech's spot welder is old and good. They haven't a clue who made it because the writing on the side is in 'Foreign'! It's excellent, though, and seen here fitted with wheel arch welding electrodes that slip inside the inner lip and weld the outer to it.

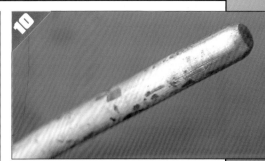

The electrode points should be rounded with a flattened tip, kept clean with a file and smoothed with fine emery paper.

Pieces of material to be spot welded together should be clean and bright, with no traces of paint. You can, however, coat both pieces with a weld through zinc primer, helping to prevent corrosion.

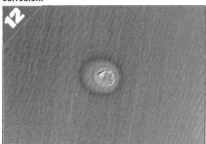

First, set the controls to a low setting and try making a spot weld. This is the aim, an even round circle of weld. If the heat setting is too high, the metal will glow red. A slight wisp of welding smoke should be seen.

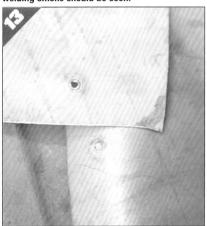

When you've completed spotting the trial piece, try to pull it apart. It should be difficult to break, requiring a lot of pulling backwards and forwards to snap. The core of the weld should be left intact on one piece, with a hole where the weld was on the other. If your weld snaps, it's too weak so you need to turn up the timer control. Do this in small stages, breaking the weld and observing.

TIG WELDING

Why Heliarc or TiG (Tung-sten Inert Gas) welding hasn't caught on in pro-fessional bodyshops, like MiG has, is a mystery. TiG is extremely versatile, and operates on a similar prin-cipal to gas welding – but doesn't have the down sides – it's not as dangerous as an open flame, produces less distortion in less-practised hands and, like MiG welding, is a lot more user-friendly.

TiG also produces smoother, cleaner welds than MiG and will weld thinner section too. If you buy the right ma-chine, you can switch from AC current to DC, enabling you to weld different materials with ease. Why, then, do most people think that a TiG is only suitable for heavy gauge material, which it does easily with less preparation?

TiG welding is probably the most versatile form of welding available and, no-doubt, will eventually replace MiG. Could it be that MiG is more popular than TiG because you need fewer hands, or is it just that the machines are not within the reach of everyone yet?

WHAT IS TIG WELDING?

TiG welding is a bit like a cross between gas welding and MiG. It's similar to MiG in that it uses an electric arc to melt the metal and form a pool but, like gas, the torch is held in one hand whilst the filler rod is in the other. This is inserted into the pool to bridge the gap between the two surfaces being welded. Like gas, it's possible to TiG weld without a filler rod. If you have two surfaces that mate with a good joint, you can just fuse the two to-gether. Practice produces clean smooth welds that can be ground down without needing filler.

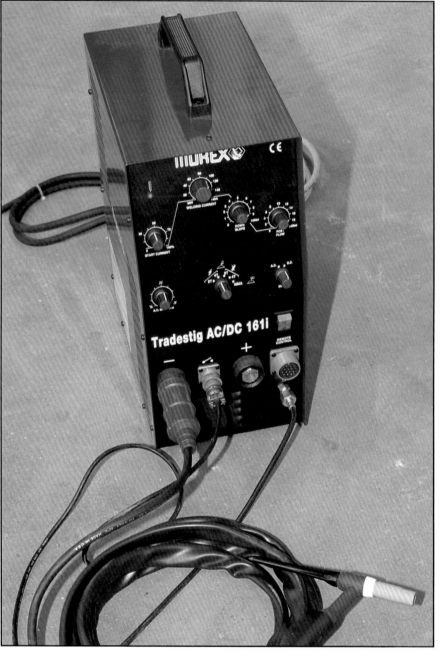

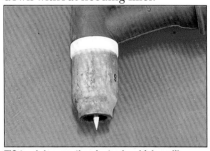

TiG torch houses the electrode which, unlike MiG, is not consumable. It's made from tungsten and needs to be sharpened to a point for use on mild steel or rounded for aluminium welding.

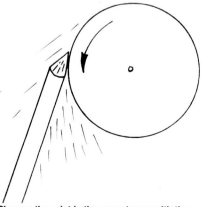

Sharpen the point in the correct way; with the grains of the metal running vertically. To do this you need to hold the tip on the bench grinder like this. Run the tip the other way and you'll get an erratic arc that's hard to control.

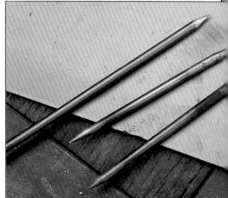

Tips need to be Thoreated Tungsten for mild steel; Zarconiated Tungsten for aluminium. Shown from left to right; a normal pointed tip for steel, a rounded Zarconiated tip and a well-abused Thoreated tip.

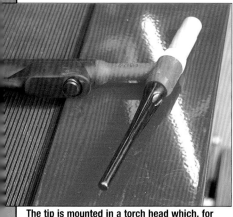

The tip is mounted in a torch head which, for really heavy duty, can be water-cooled. It is shrouded in inert Argon gas, protecting the weld and tungsten electrode from oxidation and contamination from the air; acting in a similar way to flux in gas welding. The gas is either helium, hence the heli part of heliarc (brown bottle), or more commonly, Argon (green bottle).

It's a common belief that you can use gas welding filler rods for TiG; actually it's the other way round. Proper TiG welding rods are double de-oxidised and have their ends flattened with their British Standard code, BS2901 stamped into them. These put less oxygen into the metal (too much and you'll get pops in the weld, which makes them look like an Aero bar and will weaken the structure).

A good TiG welder should feature a wide heat range so it can be controlled to weld the thinnest material – almost tin foil in some cases – but increased to weld thick chassis section.

But one of the most versatile features of the TiG is that the heat is concentrated. This means you can successfully weld thin material onto thick. It's done by concentrating the heat towards the thicker material and letting the two flow together. You'd have to practise a great deal to get these results with any other form of welding.

TIG WELDING IN PRACTICE

Welding mild steel requires a pointed tip, protruding from the shroud by about 2-3mm.

The best way to set the gas flow, is to turn it on until you can just hear the gas coming out. Then brush the torch past your face and you should ever-so slightly be able to feel the gas coming out. Ideally, you need a flow meter reading of about 6-7-litres of flow per minute.

We showed welding a butt joint in the MiG welding section, so this time it's a lap joint. The technique is very similar for TiG – clamp the two pieces together, tack, but clamp loose sections down, before seam welding in short lengths. Otherwise the pieces will curl and join up with the bit you started with! Set the TiG to around 50A and start tacking the strip together. Again, like MiG, check the machine settings first on a scrap piece of steel, the same thickness you'll be using. You only need to tack every 2½-3 inches this time.

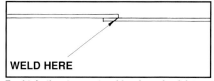

WELD HERE

To obtain the strongest weld, using a lap joint, you should aim to melt the bottom corner (arrowed) and feed the filler rod into the molten pool. Weld the top, however, and the joint won't have any strength – it'll snap.

Once you've finished tacking, don't be in a hurry to take the torch away. It's best to leave it with the gas running, preventing the weld from being contaminated by the air and oxidising.

This is what you're aiming for, a nice clean weld, which is smooth and even. Turn it over and...

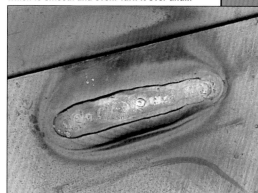

...you can see the weld has penetrated the two pieces of metal, just breaking through the other side.

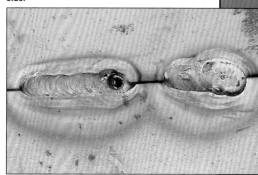

There are basically two ways to get TiG welding wrong; welding too fast, which is the same as welding with not enough amps, or welding too slow, the same as welding with too many amps. You have to be careful to avoid windy days too because the gas can be blown away from your weld, creating the same effect as too much current. The moral is, weld in a sheltered area. Here, the TiG has been set far too high and you can see how the weld has eaten into the steel, cutting a hole in the top piece.

Turn this over and you'll see too much penetration, with a blob of weld at the end. Note that the build up has actually blown out at the tip.

This weld has been produced with too few amps. Note how the weld forms a big sausage, sitting on top of the steel. When you turn it over...

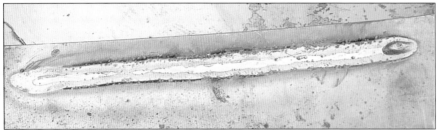

...there's little or no penetration at all because all the weld's still on top. This is definitely not how to do it!

Galvanised steel needs a bit of respect if you don't want to end up killing yourself and, as we all know, death can be fatal! You need to grind off the Zinc coating in the area of the weld. If you don't, the welding burns the zinc, giving off poisonous fumes. Note the cloud of gas being given off – very nasty!

USING TIG TO WELD CHASSIS SECTIONS

Because TiG welding has concentrated heat and excellent penetration properties, you don't need quite so much preparation as with TiG or gas welding. You can weld a length of ⅛in wall box section in one pass – something that would need two with MiG. The joint will be a lot cleaner too.

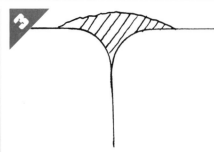

Box section only needs a 'J-prep', which basically means you only have to round the corners over, as opposed to vee-ing, which you'd need with any other form of welding.

Here we are welding a section of chassis which forms part of the rear kick up section for a race car. The joint is a butt mitre and it's laid out on top of a full-size diagram, drawn on the steel-topped work bench.

It's firmly clamped down so that it won't move, and tacked at each opposite corner.

The clamps can actually be taken off to finish-weld, but do one side first; turn it over and do the other, followed by the top, then the bottom.

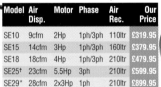

GAS WELDING

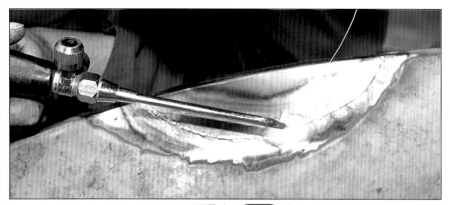

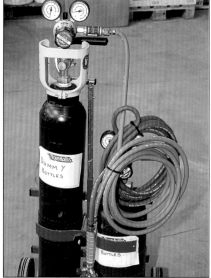

There are two separate hoses for oxygen and acetylene which should be clipped together so they don't get tangled. They're colour-coded too, blue or black for oxygen and red for acetylene. Further idiot-proofing gives acetylene fittings a left-handed thread.

EQUIPMENT NEEDED

Gas welding is the preferred method of traditional coach builders. However, it's largely been made obsolete in the modern bodyshop by MiG welders, which are more convenient. Let's face it, you can leave the MiG on and pick it up when you need it. Try doing that with a welding torch and the chances of burning you or the workshop down are very real. You'll see gas bottles in a workshop but generally the welding torch is used as a source of heat for cutting/dismantling purposes rather than welding.

But mastering the art of gas welding without distorting the surrounding panel work is going to put you well into craftsman territory. If you have any sense of perfectionism then surely it's a skill worth acquiring. To watch somebody such as Dave Gardner at Classic Metal Shaping wielding an Oxyacetylene torch on a vintage car body is a true joy because the man is incredibly talented. Not only is the equipment used to weld, but shrinkage of distorted panels is possible, too.

LIGHTING THE TORCH AND GETTING STARTED

Turn the gas on and set the pressure. In theory, you need about 2psi for the 1mm thickness of steel we'll be using. But once you get accustomed, you'll set your own pressure level.

Gas welding uses two gases which, when mixed together, produce a flame capable of melting metal. We'll be concentrating on mild steel, the only relevant metal used on modern car bodies. Oxygen and Acetylene are mixed in controlled amounts to melt mild steel at 2,700F (1,462C). The gases are supplied in separate bottles, black denotes oxygen, whilst Acetylene is maroon. It's best to have your gas bottles mounted on a cart so the equipment can be wheeled around the workshop. One advantage that gas has over arc welding in that it doesn't rely on being plugged into the wall. You could therefore gas weld almost anywhere – in the middle of a field if you like! It's important to have long leads from the torch to the bottles. 25ft is ideal, letting you get in and around your car.

The gas is controlled by a regulator on each bottle, since the pressure in the tank is far higher than you'll require at the end of the torch. For commercial use a double-diaphragm pressure regulator is best. There will be two gauges, one reading bottle pressure, the other line pressure to the end of the torch. How much pressure you'll need depends on the job you're undertaking and the torch tip size (more on this later).

The gas is turned on at the torch, then adjusted again at the bottle.

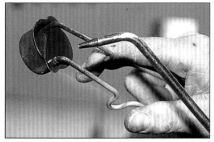

Turn on the Acetylene then light the torch with a striker, never an open flame! Flint strikers are very cheap, whilst cigarette lighters are dangerous, especially disposable ones. They've been known to go up like a grenade and are quite capable of taking your hand off – don't use them!

ADJUSTING THE TORCH AND GETTING A NEUTRAL FLAME

Turn the Acetylene on first and adjust until the sooty smoke disappears.

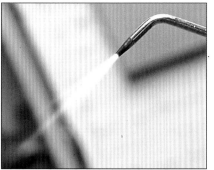

Then slowly introduce some oxygen and adjust the inner tip until it just disappears.

GAS WELDING IN PRACTICE

Wayne at Classic Metal Shaping showed us how they would tackle a repair on this rusted Morris Minor rear wing. You can see the lip is badly eaten away and, to make a satisfactory repair, Wayne recommends cutting a semi-circular patch and gas welding it in place.

First Wayne cleans the area to be welded with a clean-'n'-strip type disc mounted in an air powered die grinder.

Classic Metal Shaping make restoration panels and whole bodies for vintage cars, so their patch sections are made the traditional way; on an English wheel...

....then scribed into the wing like this.

It's important to get a good close fit with no gaps for successful gas welding. Wayne's intention is to fuse the two sections of metal together without the use of a filler rod.

CARBURIZING FLAME

LARGE LIGHT BLUE CONE
— COARSE FEATHERED EDGE
BLUE COLOUR WITH WHITE TINGE
VERY LIGHT-GREEN OUTER FEATHER

NEUTRAL FLAME

LIGHT – BLUE CONE
WIDE COARSE FEATHERED END
BLUE WITH WHITE TINGE

To weld mild steel, you will need a neutral flame. This means that equal parts of the two gases are burning together. There are two other types of flames; carburising and oxidising, but they're not used for steel.

OXIDISING FLAME

LOUD HISSING SOUND
SMALL WHITE CONE
BLUE WITH WHITE TINGE

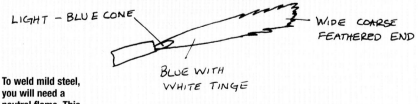
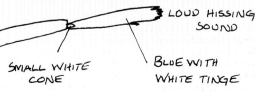

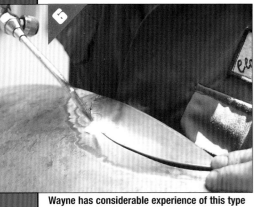

Wayne has considerable experience of this type of work and prefers to tack the two pieces together without the use of clamps. He doesn't use gloves either – which is his personal preference and not something we'd recommend – he likes to manipulate the patch into place as he's tacking it. He says not to worry at this stage if things don't line up too much at the other end of where you're tacking...

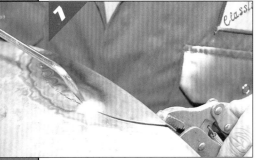

...you 'feed' the patch into the area as you go. If you've made your patch correctly, the two will mate together! Note that towards the end of tacking the patch Wayne is using a pair of fine nose Mole grips to hold the panel.

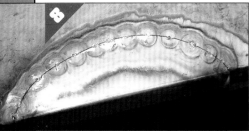

To fuse the two surfaces together, introduce some heat until they form a molten pool. You will find that they will then just flow together. Obviously this takes practice and the process of tacking is very quick; it only takes a second or two. You will see a round heat band form around the tack – so place your next tack on the edge of the first and work your way around the patch, leaving each tack time to cool and the metal to shrink back into place.

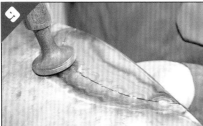

Once the whole area's tacked, you can plannish the welds flat with a hammer and dolly. The beauty of gas is that the welds are of the same hardness as the material you're working with; so you can hammer them flat. You can't do this with MiG because the filler rod's harder than the surrounding material. Plannishing an arc weld is more likely to break it since they're more brittle than gas welds.

Once the area is fully tacked, Wayne fuses the patch together in one pass. If you've tacked the area sufficiently, you shouldn't get any distortion.

Next, the area is plannished with a hammer and dolly, lightly sanded and the panel's ready for paint.

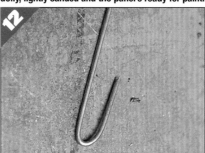

For this type of repair, Wayne didn't use a filler rod, since he didn't have a gap to fill, nor did he leave the torch in one area too long; blowing a hole. If you need to add material, a ready fluxed rod is inserted into the pool of molten metal, fusing the two pieces together. It is common practice to bend the end of the filler rod over. This has two purposes; one to stop you poking your eye out, plus you'll know which end is hot!

GAS WELDING MISTAKES

Wayne did some samples of how not to weld which, for him, went against the grain somewhat! Here he's welded a section which looks fine on the top but when you turn it over...

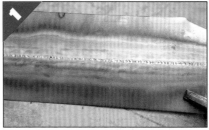

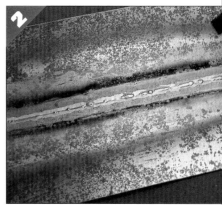

...there's no penetration – the weld will snap. Cause is moving the torch too fast.

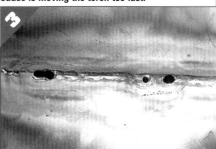

The opposite is moving the torch too slowly, causing a large heat build-up and blow-holes in the weld.

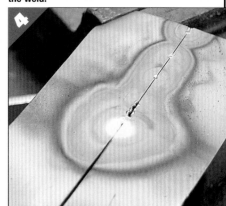

Too much heat and erratic tacks will cause the gap to expand and pull apart. In extreme cases, the two mating surfaces will actually pull under each other.

Too much heat and filler rod will cause 'Pigeon shit' welding; it will look reasonable on the top but when you turn it over...

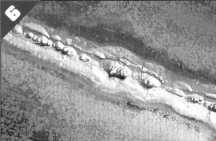

...way too much penetration and loads of weld dripping from the bottom.

From the publishers of *Tractor* magazine, *Car Mechanics* and *Stationary Engine*:

CLASSIC and Vintage COMMERCIALS

JUNE 1999 £2.40
Volume 4 Number 10

CLASSIC and Vintage COMMERCIALS

HCVS London to Brighton

GSK 223

AEC Mandator Restoration
Eden Valley Classic

A n exciting new magazine covering the whole fascinating world of historic commercials – veteran, vintage and classic. Concentrated coverage on petrol and diesel, from heavy to light. Edited by the 'lively' Peter Love. An A4 format, 48 pages, including colour. Contents include:-

- Restoration features ● A-Z of British Historic Commercials (by Nick Baldwin)
- Show and run reports ● Recent discoveries ● Classics still at work today
- Technical features ● Light commercial section ● Sale reports ● Models
- Historic commercials in their day ● Clubs coverage and support
- Events calendar ● Book and video reviews, news...and much more.

Available from leading Newsagents. **Price £2.40.**
Available on subscription **£26.00** *UK;* **£33.00** *Europe;* **£38.00** *Rest of the World.*
Back numbers **£3.00 UK;** **£3.20 Europe;** **£3.50 RoW.** *Sample copy* **£2 UK, £3** *Overseas.*

Available from high street retailers and Kelsey Publishing Ltd, PO Box 13,
Westerham, Kent TN16 3WT. Tel: 01959 541444. Fax: 01959 541400

BEST VALUE FOR MONEY CLASSIC & VINTAGE COMMERCIAL MAGAZINE

Tractor & Machinery

The monthly magazine for all tractor enthusiasts

Covers the whole tractor enthusiast scene.

RESTORATIONS, RALLIES, PLOUGHING MATCHES AUCTIONS, RUNS & CLUB EVENTS

The magazine also carries:
A-Z OF TRACTORS (a long-running part-work), TRACTOR-DRIVEN EQUIPMENT, TRACTOR HISTORIES, NEWS, LETTERS and a strong FOR SALE / WANTS SECTION.

"Tractor" is published monthly, A4 format with 64 pages including some in colour. Its lively 100 per cent tractor-related content has ensured an unprecedented demand for it since it was launched in November 1994. Edited by Peter Love.

The ***A-Z of Tractors*** is the first-ever comprehensive guide to all tractors (worldwide). It is compiled by famous vintage vehicle historian Nick Baldwin and has already ensured that readers cannot afford to miss a single issue.

Tractor is published by Kelsey Publishing Ltd.

Cover price £2.50. Available on annual subscription (12 issues) at **£24.50** UK/Eire; **£31.00** Europe 'airlifted'; **£36.00** Rest of World.
Kelsey Publishing Ltd, PO Box 13, Westerham, Kent TN16 3WT.
Tel: 01959 541444. Fax: 01959 541400.

THE WORLD'S BEST-SELLING VINTAGE TRACTOR MAGAZINE
JUNE 1999 Volume 5 Issue 7 £2.50

Tractor & Machinery
FOR THE TRACTOR ENTHUSIAST, COLLECTOR & RESTORER

JAMES COWARD'S SECMIA
JAYNE LOVE IN FLORIDA
NATIONAL ROAD RUN
JL 7857
DR HAIG'S ALLIS B RESTORATION

BUYING WELDING EQUIPMENT

Most welding equipment has shrunk in size. You don't need a lorry equipped with a Hiab to pick one up anymore, and you'll have some change in your pocket too – all thanks to invertor technology. What used to be mistaken for the NatWest building sitting in the corner of the workshop is now the size of something you put your sandwiches in.

Most machines, however, are aimed at the occasional DIY user, which is now a massive market. Most, especially MiGs, are made in Italy and sometimes in the same factory to boot; the brand name's the only difference. These machines represent excellent value for money and, to be quite honest, are capable of being used regularly. They do, however, have a limited life expectancy and are not intended to be used for constant regular heavy duty/professional use.

Look at the duty cycle. Although not too much of a worry for occasional usage, it is a good guide to a machine's quality and some work, such as batch-production of, say, exhaust systems, requires a decent duty cycle. Expressed as a percentage, it refers to the amount of time you can hold full power before letting the machine cool down.

Comparison time is usually ten minutes so, for example, a 300amp machine with a 60% duty cycle, can be used for six minutes on full power out of every ten before letting it cool down. Duty cycle is proportional; set the machine to half-power and you can halve the cool down period.

To guide you through the jungle of machines which are beckoning to blow a hole right through your pocket, you need to consider the following points:

MIGS

A give-away pointer to a good machine, is a Euro torch fitting. This enables you to swap torches if regular use makes yours uncomfortable. Garage environments mean things get broken, pipes get kinked, run over and generally abused, so it's best to have fittings which are replaceable.

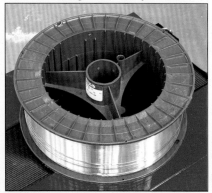

Make sure your potential purchase will take a full 15kg roll of wire, not just the small ones you can buy in the DIY store. You might think small rolls are cheaper because you're only going to be using the machine occasionally, right? But, do your homework and you'll find a 5Kg roll will cost £12-13 whilst 15Kg rolls are only a fiver more. Again, a quick way of checking whether the machine's man enough.

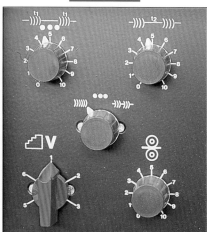

If you're going to be using the MiG for car bodywork, a very handy feature is a stitch and spot facility, with a timer.

Make sure you can mount a full bottle of gas on the back of the machine. Like buying wire, it's cheaper to buy your gas in bulk. But, make sure your potential machine is capable of holding a full bottle and wheeling it around.

This is a Murex Autolynx 161 MiG, aimed specifically at the motor trade. It takes a full-size wire reel, has a Eurotorch fitting and a duty cycle of 100% at 60amps, so it's ideal for continuous work on sheet steel. Price is £555.

A more heavy duty machine with additional features, such as stitch and spot, is the Murex Tradesmig 245. It's a about as heavy as you'd ever need to go and has a 60% duty cycle at 110amps. Price is around £1,250 plus VAT.

TIG

TiG welders are dearer than a MiG welder, so look for a decent amount of facilities on the machine. We'll take a look at the front panel of this Murex Tradestig AC/DC 161i TiG welder and explain some of the functions which are relevant to car bodywork.

Most lighter duty TiGs run off a normal single-phase supply. But make sure your unit is fitted with a 16A slow fuse. Don't be tempted to just whack in a 13A household fuse and hope. Starting off at high currents means blown fuses and, if you're unlucky, the circuit board too. Welding machines might be getting lighter thanks to inverter technology, but the down side is they're full of printed circuit boards which need protecting!

This example of a TiG welder has everything you need for car bodywork and will set you back around £2,295 plus VAT.

WELDING CURRENT

Unlike a MiG welder, where you have to guess, this TiG actually tells you what current you've set, right up to 160A.

START CURRENT

This is a sort of soft-start facility. Instead of going in with all guns blazing on full amperage, this facility will start with a percentage of the current you've set and build up to full power. The scale is marked in percentage rate and the feature is used especially on edge work; insuring against blowing a hole in your panel before you've even started welding.

DOWN SLOPE

Set in a scale of seconds, up to 10, this is the reverse of start current. When you take your finger off the trigger, the torch will wind down to zero, over the time period set, allowing you to finish off neatly without fear of blowing holes.

POST FLOW

Again, once you've taken your finger off the trigger, this adjusts how long the gas

The space age-style Murex Transtig DC 160i is a DC only machine with an easy to read digital read-out and touch control buttons. It's very compact; you can carry it around using just one arm instead of four! Price is similar at £2,300 plus VAT.

stays running. This feature is especially useful when welding oxidising materials such as aluminium, but isn't necessary for mild steel.

AC/DC SWITCHABLE

If you want to weld materials other than mild and stainless steel, you'll need an AC supply. This unit is capable of running both.

CONTROL SWITCH

This unit has a control switch allowing you to set the machine for stick welding and for two-touch or four-touch TiG welding.

Sounds complicated but all it means is that you can set the machine so you hold the torch button down to weld (2T) and release it to stop. Or 4T, where you click on and release, and the machine will continuously weld until you click off to stop.

If you're thinking the outlay for a TiG is rather high, fear not, because there is an alternative. If you've got an old Arc welder don't be in too much of a hurry to join that Sunday queue for the Council Dump because with a Scratch kit, you can convert it to a TiG welder. Okay, the results are going to depend on how good your Arc is, but this is a cheaper alternative to a full on TiG unit, especially if you're only going to be an occasional user.

What you do is connect the torch to the negative terminal whilst the earth strap goes to the positive. A special torch is supplied with the kit, with a manual valve to turn the gas on and off replacing the gas solenoid. For about half the price of pucker TiG welding machine, you could buy one of these – a top quality arc welder such as the Murex Tradesarc 131i at £665 plus VAT and a scratch kit at £225 plus VAT.

Obviously, you don't have the high frequency facility on this unit, so you have to scratch the electrode on the surface to get it started – hence the name. But it's a small price to pay to get you up and running in TiG welding.

GAS

One major reason why gas welding is losing popularity is that technically it's illegal to keep Oxygen and Acetylene bottles at home. It doesn't seem to stop anyone but you'll be having your insurance salesman rubbing his hands with glee.

Truth is, Acetylene mixed with air in the right proportions is highly explosive. If you've got a leak, you'll get no warning, a gas bottle will just explode, and take your house with it!

So, ideally you need to be in industrial premises and you've either got to be a professional or very serious about your car restoration to have these. Consequently there is a lot of good quality used gas welding equipment on the market, which may look very tempting, but before you lash out and buy the stuff, make sure you can get a supply of gas first.

Whatever you buy, there are certain things you must observe:

By law all gas welding equipment must be fitted with a one-way valve, which prevents a flame travelling back up the lead and igniting the bottle. Early Portapaks didn't have this feature and potentially they're lethal. If you don't buy equipment with a cart, you must securely chain the bottles to the wall. If you don't and the bottle falls over, knocking the top off, you've got a rocket!

In a couple of years' time, all gas welding bottles will be filled to 300 Bar. So, you need a regulator to cope with this. Make sure the equipment you buy is already up to spec unless you want to be buying a new regulator in two years' time.

In reality, there has always been only one make of readily available professional gas welding equipment; BOC/Murex. Best value is to buy your equipment as a complete set, it's just the size of the bottles and torch that vary, plus of course the cost. A complete Portapak including cart (but no gas) will set you back about £400.

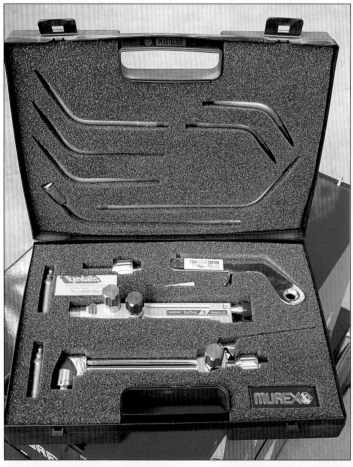

This Sapphire 5 welding and cutting torch set should have everything you need at £283 plus VAT.

BUYING GAS

Forget DIY bottles of gas, it's far more cost-effective to buy it in bulk. We took a trip to Ludlows of Luton, a typical local supplier (01582 729883), to get some prices on renting and filling gas bottles, large and small.

There are three sizes of bottle available for rent; the largest known as L-size (surprise, surprise), medium – MD30 and small – PT10 all cost around £49 for a year's rental or £4.10 monthly. You have an extra option for the PT10 because it's aimed at the DIY user so you can rent the bottle on a five year contract for £101.12, which if you work it out is considerably cheaper.

All the above prices are for gas other than Acetylene, which will cost around £65 a year or £5.45 monthly.

Prices to fill the bottle up are as follows:

GAS	L-SIZE	MD30	PT 10
Cougar (Argon mix for MiG)	£26-35	19.50	15.50
Argon	£46	£36	£20
Oxygen	£13	£11	£12
Acetylene	£43	£31	£26

SAFETY

Welding is extremely dangerous. There's no getting away from the fact that if you don't take adequate precautions, you're going to end up doing yourself potentially serious harm or burning down your workshop.

So, you need to observe some basic safety rules, take care, and obviously have a first aid kit with plenty of burn cream! Don't work where there are loads of people and make observers shield their eyes. Arc-eye is horrendous!

Workshops are home to all sorts of equipment, and the nature of the work demands flammable materials such as thinners and petrol. If you can, it's best to weld out in the open, away from confined spaces and storage of vapours. Obviously, keeping a clear workshop helps, there's nothing worse or more dangerous than trying to work whilst treading over a sea of tools on the floor.

A good range of fire extinguishers are a must, and make sure they're maintained; an annual service contract doesn't cost much – trying to operate an out of date fire extinguisher might seem trivial but it's serious when the thing doesn't work and your car's going up in flames.

A good welding helmet is obvious and a basic one will cost around £16. However, you'll be surprised how many people just close their eyes, especially when tacking! Helmets can be very awkward in practice, because you have to keep taking the thing on and off to see what you're doing. Some have a flip-up glass at the front but a better bet, especially if you're going to be serious about your welding, is to invest in the latest in electronic wizardry; a light reacting welding helmet.

This is an ESAB Eyetech helmet costing around £175, which is a lot, but once you've used one, you won't want anything else. The glass at the front is totally clear, but when you pull the trigger on your welding torch, the glass reacts with the spark and instantly turns dark. This model has a rechargeable battery, which energises itself from the arc.

Protection of the vehicle you're working on is important too. These safety blankets help to absorb stray sparks and will also keep MiG spatter off windows – have you ever finished welding your car only to find bits of molten metal stuck to the screen?

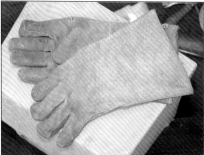

A good pair of leather gloves is essential. Many professionals weld without and most get burnt hands! The same goes for overalls – it might be a hot day when you're welding but wear a fireproof overall. Arc welders give off ultra-violet light and if you don't cover up completely you'll get a sun tan! Also, pay particular attention to the bottoms of the legs; don't tuck them in your boots because welding spatter does find its way into your feet, and hurts like hell! So make sure your overalls have long legs, so they go over your boot tops.

WHEN TO USE WHICH TYPE OF WELDING

Welding is not only about technique, but the right equipment coupled with lots of practice. On first observation, it seems a very violent process; there's loads of heat involved and molten metal, in the form of spatter, flying about all over the place.

But, it doesn't need to be. Relax and take control. Practise, and welding becomes natural. Familiarise yourself with the equipment and the mystique will vanish. Follow the guide and always buy the best machine you can afford. My own MiG cost an arm and a leg but it never breaks down, it's still going very strong after ten years and I've never regretted the purchase.

There's a strong case for all types of welding and in truth none are obsolete; it's knowing when to use them that's the key. The ideal solution is to have every type of welding equipment but that's not reality, so most are going to opt for a least one, if not two, type(s).

As a guide, I can only repeat the words of Wayne Twinn at Classic Metal Shaping: *"If the panel's not structural and you can get to both sides to beat it out, use gas. If you can't, it's structural or double skinned, use MiG or TiG."* – It's as simple as that!

Happy Welding!

ACKNOWLEDGEMENTS

We'd like to thank the following people and companies for helping to compile this supplement:

DARREN ARIS & MARC SPRATLEY
Randalls Engineering, Welding
Industrial Hygiene and Safety Centre,
Selbourne Road, Luton, Beds LU4 8NX
01582 573281/5

DEAN & PHIL THE WELDER
Autokraft Crash Repairs,
Goodmayes Lane, Ilford, Essex 1G3 9QA
0181 597 9424

DAVE GARDNER & WAYNE TWINN
Classic Metal Shaping,
Walton on the Naze, Essex
01255 850253

IAN HUCKLEBRIDGE & PAUL DELL
SprayTech, Kemps Farm, Ford,
Aylesbury, Bucks
01296 747796

PETER WILLS
Ludlow's of Luton, Windmill Trading Estate,
Thistle Road, Luton, Beds
01582 729883

Welding Equipment and Supplies Availability Chart

SUPPLIER	Gas Welding Equipment	Gas Welding Consumables	Arc Welding Equipment	Arc Welding Consumables	MIG Welding Equipment	Mig Welding Consumables	TIG Welding Equipment	TIG Welding Consumables	Plasma Cutters	Safety Wear	Tools & Accessories
CLARKE INTERNATIONAL Hemnall Street Epping Essex CM16 4LG Tel: 01992 565300 Fax: 01992 561562 E-mail: sales@clarkeint.com Web: www.clarkeint.com		Clarke	Clarke	Clarke	Clarke	Clarke	Clarke	Clarke	Clarke	Clarke	Clarke
MACHINE MART 211 Lower Parliament Street Nottingham NG1 1GN Tel: 0115 956 5555 Fax: 0115 988 1212 E-mail: sales@machinemart.co.uk Web: www.machinemart.co.uk	Clarke	Clarke		Clarke	Clarke	Clarke		Clarke	Clarke	Clarke Turton Dickies	Clarke Facom Stanley Paramo Black & Decker Bosch DeWalt Skil Makita
SEALEY GROUP Kempson Way Suffolk Business Park Bury St Edmonds Suffolk IP32 7AR Tel: 01284 757500 Fax: 01284 703534 E-mail: sales@sealey.co.uk	Sealey Power Welders	Sealey Power Welders	Sealey Power Welders	Sealey Power Welders	Sealey Power Welders	Sealey Power Welders	Sealey Power Welders	Sealey Power Welders	Sealey Power Welders	Sealey Power Welders	Sealey
T F KELLER 24 Cattle Market Street Norwich Norfolk NR1 3DY Tel: 01603 624681 Fax: 01603 663790			Draper	Draper Orlikon	Draper	Draper				North Star	Draper Moor & Wright Record Stanley.
TRANSPEED 211/213 Portland Road Hove East Sussex BN3 5LA Tel: 01273 774578 Fax: 01273 207763 E-mail: transpeed@compuserve.com Web: visitweb.com/transpeed	Maypole	Maypole	SIP Nutool Sealey Welding Star Draper	SIP Nutool Sealey Welding Star Draper	SIP Nutool Sealey Welding Star Draper Kestrel	SIP Nutool Sealey Welding Star Draper Kestrel	SIP Welding Star	SIP Welding Star	SIP Sealey	Kestrel Sealey	Draper Franklin Hilka Kamasa
WWS Protea Way Letchworth Herts SG6 1JT Tel: 01462 482200 Fax: 01462 482202 E-mail: sales@wholeweld.co.uk Web: www.wholeweld.com	Weldability	Weldability	Telwin	Weldability	Telwin	Weldability	Telwin	Weldability	Telwin	Weldability	Weldability